Lab Manual
to Accompany

Fundamentals of Electronics: DC Circuits
Volume I

Ernest Arney

ITT Technical Institute

Delmar Publishers

an International Thomson Publishing company I(T)P®

Albany · Bonn · Boston · Cincinnati · Detroit · London · Madrid · Melbourne
Mexico City · New York · Pacific Grove · Paris · San Francisco · Singapore
Tokyo · Toronto · Washington

NOTICE TO THE READER

Delmar Staff:
Publisher: Alar Elken
Acquisitions Editor: Gregory Clayton
Developmental Editor: Michelle Ruelos Cannistraci
Production Manager: Larry Main
Art and Design Coordinator: Nicole Reamer
Marketing Coordinator: Paula Collins
Editorial Assistant: Amy Tucker

Online Services

Delmar Online
To access a wide variety of Delmar products and services on the World Wide Web, point your browser to:
http://www.delmar.com/delmar.html
or email: info@delmar.com

thomson.com
To access International Thomson Publishing's home site for information on more than 34 publishers and 20,000 products, point your browser to:
http://www.thomson.com
or email: findit@kiosk.thomson.com

A service of I(T)P®

COPYRIGHT © 2000
By Delmar Publishers
a division of International Thomson Publishing

The ITP logo is a trademark under license.

Printed in Canada

For more information, contact:

Delmar Publishers
3 Columbia Circle, Box 15015
Albany, New York 12212-5015

International Thomson Publishing Europe
Berkshire House
168-173 High Holborn
London WC1V 7AA
United Kingdom

Nelson ITP, Australia
102 Dodds Street
South Melbourne
Victoria, 3205 Australia

Nelson Canada
1120 Birchmont Road
Scarborough, Ontario
Canada, M1K 5G4

International Thomson Publishing France
Tour Maine-Montparnasse
33 Avenue du Maine
75755 Paris Cedex 15, France

International Thomson Editores
Seneca 53
Colonia Polanco
11560 Mexico D. F. Mexico

International Thomson Publishing GmbH
Königswinterer Strasse 418
53227 Bonn
Germany

International Thomson Publishing Asia
60 Albert Street
#15-01 Albert Complex
Singapore 189969

International Thomson Publishing—Japan
Hirakawacho Kyowa Building, 3F
2-2-1 Hirakawacho
Chiyoda-ku, Tokyo 102
Japan

ITE Spain/Paraninfo
Calle Magallanes, 25
28015-Madrid, Espana

7 8 9 10 XXX 08 07 06

ISBN: 0-7668-3185-X

Contents

Volume I

DC Fundamentals

The experiments in this manual are designed to accompany *Fundamentals of Electronics: DC/AC Circuits* by David Terrell. The experiments have the same progression and conventions as the text. The experiments start at an introductory level and advance to several different levels of complexity. There are sufficient projects to provide beneficial experiments in any course offering DC or AC circuits.

All beginning and advanced electronics students can benefit from the Manual to accomplish these outcomes:

- test equipment mastery

- use observations to learn and support theory concepts

- learn troubleshooting skills

- improve critical thinking skills (putting several facts together to arrive at a conclusion)

Introductory experiments that introduce how to properly use each piece of test equipment are included as experiments. Oscilloscope introduction including screen pictorials of what the student should see on the oscilloscope are also included in some of the AC circuit experiments.

Organization

The **Objectives** of each experiment are stated to ensure the student understands what is to be learned. The objectives should be reviewed before and after the experiment is completed.

In the **Text Reference,** the textbook reference is given for each experiment. Use the text and look at the referenced material **before** doing an experiment. This will confirm what was learned in theory and aid in writing observations about what was observed while completing procedures.

The **Introduction** will review theory and introduce important concepts that will be learned about how to use the test equipment to accomplish certain procedural steps. Other information within the Introduction will include useful equations and troubleshooting techniques.

The **Procedures** are written for step-by-step guidance in early experiments, in later projects the steps are decreased but are sufficient to ensure the correct conclusions are observed by the student.

The last area of each experiment is the **Observations**. The Observations are practical questions based on the observations made during the course of the experiment. The observations are mixed in with the Procedures to ensure the student uses the circuit to answer questions about circuit operation, and can see what actually happens if circuit parameters change. With this type of observation the student can make the change and directly observe what happens. Rather than answering questions after the circuit has been disconnected or trying to answer the questions outside the lab environment, the questions are presented while the student is working with the circuit in the lab.

Approach

Each series of experiments will have different **Levels**, for instance, in the Series Circuit grouping there are five different levels. In the early levels the Procedures are detailed to provide "step-by-step guidance;" this will create good lab habits. Included in the Procedures are Discussions which are used to ensure that the student knows the right answer and the reason why it is the right answer. This teaches the student to make accurate observations about measurements made in the circuit and proper use of the test equipment. Suggestions on how to follow procedural steps and use equations to calculate or determine circuit values are included in the Discussions areas. Warnings about what could happen if the test equipment is not used properly are also given and emphasized.

It is not necessary that all of the projects be accomplished in a given series. However, each level becomes somewhat more challenging. As the experiments progress in levels and material, fewer procedures are given to guide the student toward the outcome. If each student uses each level correctly, the final level can be accomplished by all students.

This approach is designed to reinforce theory, discover new practical ways of looking at theory, learn to construct circuits and properly use text equipment, and troubleshoot circuits.

When experiments have been completed, allowing students to interact and discuss the results and observations is an important part of any laboratory experience. Encourage this interaction as a means of solidifying information gained from the experiments.

At the end of the Experiments Manual are single sheets of linear and semilog graph paper. Make as many copies of the graph paper as required.

The created graphs and tables could be used in a theory class to enhance visualization of concepts and theories. Having students do an experiment prior to it being presented in theory allows for "discovery" of how things work. Then, the theory can reinforce observations made in the laboratory environment. Additional experiments, using the different levels, can be accomplished in the laboratory, increasing the critical thinking skills of the students.

To the Students

When making "observations," generally there are no wrong answers as long as you write what you observed in accomplishing the procedures. Always try to make as many observations as possible, regardless of how obvious or subtle. State the observations as clearly as you can. Compare your observations with others and discuss them. Add to your list of observations what others have observed, then analyze how they fit or don't fit with yours. Relate the observations to material learned in theory: Are there differences? Are things working contrary to theory? Do your observations support and reinforce theory? Are the graphs and tables the same as discussed in theory?

Create mental images of what you observed, then begin to try to learn **why** it works this way or that way. Ask questions about those things that you do not understand; especially ask **how** or **why** this or that occurred. Doing these things will allow you to benefit from your laboratory experience.

Always preview the text material before doing the experiment. Write down any equations that may assist your completing the experiment. Then read the experiment, doing the calculations before connecting the circuits and measuring them. Carefully follow each procedural step, making sure you understand why the step is being taken. Think about what **should be** observed versus **what is being** observed.

Voltmeter; Digital Multimeter (DMM)

Name _Donivan J. McOweal_   Class _ET_   Date _06/16/06_

Objectives   Upon completion of this experiment, you should be able to:

- Use the DMM as a voltmeter.

- Adjust the DC power supply to various voltages.

Text Reference   Terrell, *Fundamentals of Electronics: DC/AC Circuits*
    Chapter 2, Section 2-2
    Chapter 9, Sections 9-2 and 9-4

Materials Required   DMM
Variable dual power supply; 0 to 20 volts dc
Various test leads

Introduction

Digital Multimeter (DMM)   The DMM is a multipurpose piece of test equipment that can be used to measure voltage, resistance, and current. Some DMMs have other special functions that can be used to test components which will be studied later.

Measuring voltage is one of the most important elements of troubleshooting and analyzing circuits. This experiment will concentrate on learning to use the DMM to measure voltage and how to adjust the dc power supply for specified voltage levels. The Operator's Manuals for the DMM and the dc power supply will assist in this process.

Although most DMMs differ somewhat, all have the same basic controls, even though the control names may not be the same. Observe the front panel of the DMM and select the voltage switch. This could be indicated by the letter **V**. There should be a switch that allows selection of either DC or AC; select **DC**. There may also be a position or a different switch that will allow the selection of a range or maximum voltage value to be measured.

Indicate what the DMM ranges are:

Some DMMs have auto-ranging, meaning that the DMM will automatically adjust for the required range. If there are no range selection switches the DMM will generally have this feature.

What is the maximum dc voltage that can be measured as indicated by the ranges? _1200 VDC_

What is the minimum dc voltage range available?

200 mVDC

Notice that the DMM has two or three input jacks. Test leads will be connected to the input jacks which will then be connected to the component under test or to measure voltage. The DMM has at least one red jack and a black jack. It could be that these input jacks are named dc and Ω (ohms) or resistance; V or volts; I or current or mAmps or common input. Each of the jacks is used for a different type of measurement.

For the purposes of the experiments in this manual, the common or black jack should generally be connected to a black lead and the volts, Ω (or resistance) or current input jack should be red.

DC Power Supply

The dc power supply will provide a variable dc voltage. The power supply should have an adjustment control for voltage and a current limit adjustment. Most dc power supplies have an analog or digital scale that indicates the approximate output voltage value. **Do not depend upon this indication for accuracy.**

Find the controls for the voltage adjustment and the current limit control.

Another type of switch which may be included on the power supply panel (for dual power supplies), is the series/parallel/independent selector switch. For the purposes of this experiment and unless otherwise directed, this switch should be set in the independent mode of operation. As the other features of the power supply are required, they will be explained.

The current limit control adjusts the maximum current level that the power supply will provide before going into a protection mode. When the power supply exceeds the current limit, it will cause the output voltage to go to zero volts. For the purposes of this experiment adjust the current limit to maximum. This should be a clockwise adjustment.

Each experiment or troubleshooting project should use one device as the **standard** or reference piece of test equipment. That way, if an error is introduced into the measurements, the same error will occur with every measurement. Therefore, voltage comparisons are easier to make. In this experiment the DMM will be the standard.

Notice that the dc power supply has two output jacks per supply. The jacks are probably red, indicating positive polarity, and black for negative polarity. Although most DMMs are not polarity sensitive, it is always good practice to observe correct polarity when connecting the voltage meter.

Some power supplies have a green jack. This jack is connected to earth ground through the ground terminal of the ac plug. We will not use this jack during this experiment.

Procedures

1. Make sure the dc power supply and the DMM are turned off. Adjust the dc power supply voltage control(s) to minimum. Adjust the current limit control(s) (if available) to maximum.

2. Connect the DMM leads to the dc power supply, connecting the red jack of the DMM to the red jack of the power supply and black jack of the DMM to the black jack of the same power supply.

Discussion   If using a dual power supply, make sure that the leads are connected to both terminals of the same supply. Make sure that the red lead is connected to the input jack of the DMM that is used to measure voltage. This should be indicated around the input jack.

---

3. Have your lab partner or other lab teams check your connections, while you check their connections.

4. Select a DMM voltage range that will allow 30 volts to be measured. Turn on the DMM and the power supply.

5. Slowly adjust the dc power supply voltage control until the maximum output voltage is indicated.

6. What is the maximum voltage value measured?

   ____32____ volts

7. Adjust the dc power supply until the DMM indicates one-half of the maximum value obtained in Step 6.

8. Have your lab partner or other lab teams check the value indicated on the DMM while you check their indicated value.

9. Have another lab team or your lab partner select voltages between 0 volts and the maximum value of the dc power supply. Now check each other to make sure that you can adjust the power supply to any required voltage value.

Discussion   When using the DMM as a voltmeter it is common to attempt to adjust the power supply to the exact value or 100% accuracy. Unless your power supply has a fine adjustment control, do not worry so much about 100% accuracy. If the adjusted value is within 10% of the intended value, move on to the next one. A lot of time will be wasted trying to get the supply voltage to exactly 100% accuracy when it may not be required.

Voltmeter; Volt-Ohm-Meter (VOM)

Name _Donivan J. McGreal_   Class_____   Date _06/16/06_

Objectives   Upon completion of this experiment, you should be able to:

- Use the linear scale of the Volt-Ohm-Meter (VOM).

- Review the controls of the power supply.

- Adjust the power supply to specific voltage levels using the volt-ohm-meter (VOM) as the standard.

Text Reference   Terrell, *Fundamentals of Electronics: DC/AC Circuits*
       Chapter 2, Section 2-2
       Chapter 9, Sections 9-1 and 9-4

Materials Required   VOM
    Variable power supply; 0 to 20 volts dc
    Various test leads

Introduction

Voltmeter   The Volt-Ohm-Meter or VOM has several ranges for DC voltage, but generally uses one scale for the ranges. Observe the scale shown in Figure 2-1. Each end of the scale (left side and right side) has dc indicated. This means that this scale is used for DC voltages and currents. This scale registers from 0 to 10 and can be used to measure DC voltages that are multiples of 10.

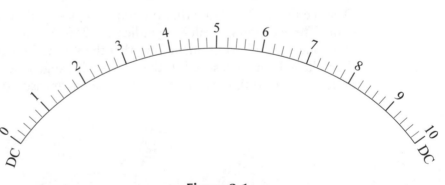

Figure 2-1

Suppose the 1-volt dc voltage range is selected. Most VOMs have a rotary switch located in the center of the meter which will indicate what is to be measured and what range or scale is to be used. This means that when the needle deflects full scale it will be at 10 on the scale. However, because the 1-volt range was selected, this would indicate that only 1 volt is being measured. If the needle deflects until it is over the 5 (half-scale deflection), 0.5 volts would be the measured voltage indicated.

If the range setting were 10 volts dc, the indication would be exactly as indicated. If the range selected were 100-volts dc and the needle deflected so that it was at the 2, 20 volts would be the measured voltage.

Still on the 100-volt range, suppose the needle deflects until it is between the 4 and 5, and is over the 2nd small increment from the 4, as indicated in Figure 2-2. Because the 100-volt range setting was selected, the amount of voltage between 4 and 5 would be 10 volts. Since the selected range is 100 volts and there are 10 divisions, each division must be 10 volts. Therefore 40 volts is being measured because the needle is beyond the 4, **plus** 2 volts per small increment or 4 volts, for a total of 44 volts.

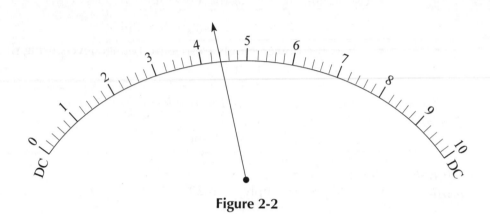

Figure 2-2

$$\frac{10\ volts}{5\ divisions} = 2\ volts/division$$

Notice that there are four lines creating five divisions between the 4 and the 5 on the scale. If there are 10 volts between the integers 4 and the 5, then the smaller division is 2 volts per division. The 2 would represent 2 volts per increment. Two increments beyond the 4 would indicate four volts plus the 40 volts indicated by the 4, for a total of 44 volts.

Observe Figure 2-3. Note that the top scale has 3 different numbers below the scale. Three different scales are indicated: 250, 50, and 10. When using this scale one would have to make sure that the selected range is used to determine the voltage being measured. If the 25-volt dc range is selected and the needle deflects at the 100, how much voltage is being measured?

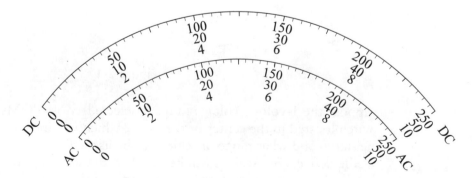

Figure 2-3

Answer   If 25 volts is the maximum that can be measured and if the needle
is pointing to the 100 on the 250 scale, then the voltage indication is
10 volts.

If the 5-volt range is selected and the needle deflects exactly midway
between the 30 and 40 on the scale, how much voltage would be
indicated?

If you stated 3.5 volts, you are correct.

Each scale represents a range of voltages that can be measured. This scale is
much more flexible than the scale in Figure 2-1, so we can use it for different
values on the same scale.

Note also that the voltmeter leads must be **across** the component, resistor, or
voltage source. The meter leads must be placed so that each end of the
component is touched by one of the leads.

Polarity is important when using a VOM. Make sure that the more positive
voltage being measured is connected to the red lead and the more negative
point to the black lead. If an unknown voltage is to be measured, always use the
highest voltage range possible to start. Then slowly decrease the range until an
accurate measurement can be made.

Procedures

1. Make sure the power supply is turned off. Turn the power supply voltage
   adjustment(s) to minimum.

2. Set the range selector switch on the VOM to the smallest whole number.

3. Connect the leads of the VOM to the output jacks of the power supply. Connect the
   red lead of the VOM to the red output jack and the black lead of the VOM to the
   black output jack.

Discussion   The VOM is polarity sensitive. If the leads are incorrectly connected, the
needle will try to deflect in the wrong direction. This could cause damage to the meter
movement within the meter. Always make sure that the VOM is connected for proper
polarity. Some VOMs have a polarity switch that allows either polarity to be measured—no
matter how the meter is connected. See if the VOM has a switch that says –DC and +DC.
Make sure that the switch is in the +DC position for this sequence of steps.

---

4. Turn on the power supply.

   What does the VOM indicate?

   - .004 volts

5. Turn off the power supply.

6. Set the VOM range selector switch to measure a voltage of about 30 volts.

Discussion   The VOM range selector switch should always be set to a higher range than the maximum voltage that can be measured. If the range is too low, the needle will deflect very rapidly to the right which could damage the meter movement. The range selector switch can always be decreased once an approximate value of voltage is known.

7. Turn on the power supply.

   Slowly adjust the power supply voltage control until the maximum output voltage is reached. If the range selector switch is set too high, select the next lowest range without causing the needle to deflect beyond the indicated scale.

   Example   Suppose the 50-volt range is selected and the indicated voltage is about 20 volts. The next lowest range is 30 volts. The 30-volt range can safely be selected. If the next lowest range is 15 volts, this range cannot be safely selected.

8. What does the VOM indicate?

   __31.9__ volts

   Discussion   Now the maximum and minimum output voltage levels of the power supply are known. This is important when an unknown voltage is to be measured. Always set the VOM range selector to measure the highest output voltage of the power supply. This will ensure that the VOM is not damaged.

9. Turn the power supply voltage adjustment to minimum.

10. Set the VOM range selector switch to measure a known voltage of 6 volts.

11. Now turn on the power supply and adjust the voltage until 6 volts is indicated by the VOM.

    Discussion   Remember that if the power supply has a meter that indicates voltage, **do not** rely on this meter for accuracy. The standard or reference device for voltage measurements is the VOM.

12. Have your lab partner or other lab teams check and see if the indicated voltage measurement is 6 volts. At the same time verify their measurement.

    __DJ__ Initials of individual(s) who checked voltage measurement.

13. Using Steps 9 through 12 as a guide, measure the following voltages. Have each voltage measurement verified by a different team or individual.

    +12 volts __+13.5__ verified by __DJ__ BS, TH, JE, TM
    +18 volts __16.0__ verified by __DJ__ BS, TH, JE, TM
    +0.75 volts __1.3__ verified by __DJ__ BS, JH, JE, TM
    +3 volts __3.1__ verified by __DJ__ BS, TH, JE, TM

Resistor Color Code

Name **Donivan McGreal**　　　　　　　Class　　　　　　Date **06/16/06**

Objectives	Upon completion of this experiment, you should be able to:
	• Learn the resistor color code.
	• Determine the stated value of a resistor by interpreting the resistor's color code.
Text Reference	Terrell, *Fundamentals of Electronics: DC/AC Circuits* Chapter 2, Sections 2-4 and 2-7
Materials Required	Ten various resistors
Note	Keep these resistors; they will be used in Experiment 4.

Introduction

For this experiment select ten different resistors from the resistor kit or use the ten different values your instructor has selected for you.

The procedure for determining the stated value is found in Chapter 2 of the text. The color code tables are repeated at the end of this experiment for your convenience. Use them to refer to, but do not allow them to become a crutch. Practice without referring to the tables and only refer to them for verification.

Procedures

1. Observe Table 3-1. Taking a given resistor, indicate the color of each band as shown in Table 3-1. Then enter the number, multiplier, or tolerance band that corresponds to the color.

   Then determine the indicated resistance value.

BAND	COLOR CODE	NUMERIC VALUE
1st Band	Brown	1
2nd Band	Black	0
3rd Band	Orange	10^3
4th Band	Gold	$+10\%$

Table 3-1

The first band is a one (1), the second band is a zero (0), the multiplier band or third band is one times ten to third power (10^3) or one thousand (1000). Multiply 10 times 1000; the example resistor shown in Table 3-1 is a 10-kΩ resistor.

2. Using each of the selected resistors, fill out each table, as shown in Table 3-1, and determine the indicated value of the resistor.

BAND	COLOR CODE	NUMERIC VALUE
1st Band	Orange	3
2nd Band	Orange	3
3rd Band	Black	10^0
4th Band	Gold	$\pm 5\%$

Table 3-2

Resistor in Table 3-2 is ~~330~~ Ω.

BAND	COLOR CODE	NUMERIC VALUE
1st Band	Orange	3
2nd Band	Orange	3
3rd Band	Brown	10^1
4th Band	Gold	$\pm 5\%$

Table 3-3

Resistor in Table 3-3 is _330_ Ω.

BAND	COLOR CODE	NUMERIC VALUE
1st Band	~~Orange~~ Green	~~3~~ 5
2nd Band	~~Orange~~ Blue	~~3~~ 6
3rd Band	Gold	10^{-1}
4th Band	Gold	$\pm 5\%$

5.6

Table 3-4

Resistor in Table 3-4 is ~~5.6~~ Ω.

BAND	COLOR CODE	NUMERIC VALUE
1st Band	Yellow	4
2nd Band	~~Purple~~ Violet	7
3rd Band	Gold	10^{-1}
4th Band	Gold	$\pm 5\%$

Table 3-5

Resistor in Table 3-5 is ___4.7___ Ω.

BAND	COLOR CODE	NUMERIC VALUE
1st Band	Green	5
2nd Band	Blue	6
3rd Band	Yellow	10^4
4th Band	Gold	$\pm 5\%$

Table 3-6

Resistor in Table 3-6 is ___560K___ Ω.

BAND	COLOR CODE	NUMERIC VALUE
1st Band	Blue	6
2nd Band	Gray	8
3rd Band	Yellow	10^4
4th Band	Gold	$\pm 5\%$

Table 3-7

Resistor in Table 3-7 is ___680K___ Ω.

BAND	COLOR CODE	NUMERIC VALUE
1st Band	Brown	1
2nd Band	Red	2
3rd Band	Gold	10^{-1}
4th Band	Gold	$\pm 5\%$

Table 3-8

Resistor in Table 3-8 is ___1.2___ Ω.

BAND	COLOR CODE	NUMERIC VALUE
1st Band	Brown	1
2nd Band	Black	0
3rd Band	Green	10^5
4th Band	Gold	±5%

Table 3-9

Resistor in Table 3-9 is ___100000___ Ω.   1Molu

BAND	COLOR CODE	NUMERIC VALUE
1st Band	Gray	8
2nd Band	Red	2
3rd Band	Yellow	10^4
4th Band	Gold	±5%

Table 3-10

Resistor in Table 3-10 is ___820 K___ Ω.

BAND	COLOR CODE	NUMERIC VALUE
1st Band	Brown	1
2nd Band	Gray	8
3rd Band	Gold	10^{-1}
4th Band	Gold	±5%

Table 3-11

Resistor in Table 3-11 is ___1.8___ Ω.

3. Suppose that the resistor in Table 3-11 does not have a fourth band. What is the tolerance?   ±20%

If the resistor were measured with a meter, what range of values could be measured and the resistor still be within tolerance.

Example   Suppose the resistor was a 10-kΩ resistor. With no fourth band the tolerance is ±20%.

$10 \text{ k}\Omega \times 0.2 = 2000 \text{ }\Omega$ Step 1
$10 \text{ k}\Omega + 2000 \text{ }\Omega = 12 \text{ k}\Omega$ Step 2
$10 \text{ k}\Omega - 2000 \text{ }\Omega = 8 \text{ k}\Omega$ Step 3

Step 1: Multiply the stated value of the resistor by 0.2.
Step 2: Add this value to the stated value.
Step 3: Subtract this value from the stated value.

So the range that the 10-kΩ resistor could be is from 12,000 ohms to 8,000 ohms. If the resistor value measures within this range, it is considered to be within tolerance.

Using resistor in Table 3-11, determine its range. Remember that no band means that the tolerance is ±20%. 1.89

High range value _~~___~~ 4JL

Low range value ___.09 JL

COLOR CODE	DIGIT VALUE	MULTIPLIER VALUE	TOLERANCE VALUE
Black	0	10^0	—
Brown	1	10^1	—
Red	2	10^2	±2%
Orange	3	10^3	—
Yellow	4	10^4	—
Green	5	10^5	—
Blue	6	10^6	—
Violet	7	—	—
Gray	8	—	—
White	9	—	—
Silver	—	—	±10%
Gold	—	—	±5%
No Tolerance Band	—	—	±20%

Ohmmeter; (DMM)

Name _Donivan Mc avest_   Class _____   Date _06/06/06_

Objectives   Upon completion of this experiment, you should be able to:

- Use the DMM as an ohmmeter.
- Read the ohms ranges.
- Determine if a resistor is within the stated tolerance.

Text Reference   Terrell, *Fundamentals of Electronics: DC/AC Circuits*
     Chapter 2, Sections 2-4 and 2-7
     Chapter 9, Section 9-5

Materials Required   DMM (Digital Multimeter)
The same 10 resistors used in Experiment 3
Various test leads

Introduction

Most Digital Multimeters (DMM) have several ranges that are used for measuring resistance values in ohms. Ranges on DMMs generally indicate the maximum resistance value that can be measured. The digital display generally indicates the kilo ohms of the component being measured. There might also be two other range selections, one that measures up to 200 ohms and a second that can be used to measure 2 megaohms or a 20-megaohms range. If the documentation (operating instructions), are available for the DMM to be used, read the section on using the ohmmeter to be sure what the display indicates.

Some DMMs have auto-ranging, meaning that the meter will automatically determine the range necessary to indicate the correct amount of resistance.

⚡**CAUTION**   **Never use an ohmmeter when power is applied to the component.**

When using an ohmmeter remember that it must be connected across the component under test. If the resistor or component is connected in a circuit, remove one leg or lead of the component to insure that only that resistor is being measured.

Procedures

1. Using the stated values of the resistors used in Experiment 3, enter those values in Table 4-1.

TABLE # FROM EXPERIMENT 3	COLOR CODE (Indicated Value)	DMM INDICATION (Measured Value)
Table 3-2	~~33 33~~ Ω	~~3.35~~ Ω
Table 3-3	330 Ω	328 Ω
Table 3-4	5.6 Ω	5.5 Ω
Table 3-5	4.7 Ω	4.6 Ω
Table 3-6	560K Ω	554K Ω
Table 3-7	680 K Ω	682K Ω
Table 3-8	1.2 Ω	1.2 Ω
Table 3-9	1.0M Ω	~~~~ 980K Ω
Table 3-10	820K Ω	821K Ω
Table 3-11	1.8 Ω	1.8 Ω

Table 4-1

2. Using the DMM as an ohmmeter, place the ohmmeter across each resistor and record the measured value in Table 4-1.

3. For each resistor listed in Table 4-1, using the tolerance band indicated in the appropriate table in Experiment 3, determine the minimum and maximum values for a good resistor. Enter the calculated data in Table 4-2.

TABLE # FROM EXPERIMENT 3	MINIMUM VALUE	MAXIMUM VALUE
Table 3-2	31.35 Ω	34.65 Ω
Table 3-3	313.5 Ω	346.5 Ω
Table 3-4	5.32 Ω	5.88 Ω
Table 3-5	4.47 Ω	4.93 Ω
Table 3-6	532 KΩ	588 KΩ
Table 3-7	646 KΩ	714 KΩ
Table 3-8	1.14 Ω	1.26 Ω
Table 3-9	950KΩ	1.05mΩ
Table 3-10	779 KΩ	861KΩ
Table 3-11	1.71 Ω	1.89 Ω

Table 4-2

Observations

1. Are all of the resistors measured within tolerance?

   Yes

2. From Table 4-1 use the measured value of the resistor listed for row Table 3-10. Determine what the percentage difference is between the stated value and the measured value.

Example   Suppose the row Table 3-10 resistor measured value is 9.97 kΩ and the indicated value is 10 kΩ.

10 kΩ – 9.97 kΩ = 30 Ω the difference between the two values (BIG – Small).

Divide by the value indicated by the color code.

$$\left(\frac{30 \ \Omega}{10 \ \text{k}\Omega} \right) 100 = 0.3\%$$

Indicate the percentage difference of the row Table 3-10 resistor from Table 4-1.

 .0012%

Ohmmeter; Volt-Ohm-Meter (VOM)

Name _Donivan McGirel_   Class _____   Date _06/23/06_

Objectives   Upon completion of this experiment, you should be able to:

- Read a non-linear analog scale.

- Use the analog ohmmeter.

- Read the ohms scale.

- Determine if a resistor is within the stated tolerance.

Text Reference   Terrell, *Fundamentals of Electronics: DC/AC Circuits*
      Chapter 2, Sections 2-4 and 2-7
      Chapter 9, Section 9-5

Materials Required   VOM

1-MΩ resistor	4.7-kΩ resistor
100-kΩ resistor	1.5-kΩ resistor
10-kΩ resistor	560-Ω resistor
8.2-kΩ resistor	Various test leads

Introduction

Note Figure 5-1. This is a typical analog scale. Previously, the linear voltage scales were used to measure the power supply voltages. Observe the very top scale and notice the non-linearity of the scale. Also note that the scale is backward from the other scales; when the other scales are at the maximum value, the scale is at zero.

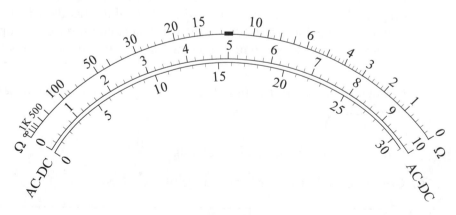

Figure 5-1

Your VOM should have several ranges used to measure ohms. These ranges should appear as X1, X10, X100, X1k, X10k, X100k or other multiples of 10.

The range that you select is the **multiplier**. Suppose that the needle is at or over the number 15 on the very top scale and the range selector is on X1k. This means that the component or resistor under test is:

$$15 \times 1k = 15,000 \ \Omega \text{ or a } 15\text{-}k\Omega \text{ resistor}$$

Also note the left end of the ohm scale. Notice how close together the marks are on this side of the scale. This makes it difficult to determine the number the needle is at or over. However, look at the center or the right hand side of the scale and notice that it is much easier to read. Therefore, the ohmmeter range selected should have the needle deflection as close to the center or right side of the scale as possible.

When the number indicated by the needle has been determined, multiply the range selected by the number indicated by the needle to get the amount of resistance in ohms.

Every time the range selector is changed the meter must be **zeroed**. We will practice this procedure before measuring any resistors.

The Operator's Manual should be helpful in completing this experiment.

Procedures

1. Connect the meter leads to the VOM.

2. Set the meter control knobs to the lowest ohm setting (X1).

3. Make sure the needle is setting on the infinity symbol, or zero for the other linear scales. If it is not, there should be an adjustment for the needle.

4. Connect the meter leads together. The needle should deflect to indicate zero (0) ohms.

   If not, there should be a zero-ohms adjustment. Adjust the control until the needle is on top of the zero (0) on the ohm scale.

   Discussion   If the meter will not zero, it may have a low battery. The Operator's Manual should tell you how to check for a low battery. If the needle will not deflect at all, the meter probably has a bad fuse or the external circuit breaker has opened. There should be a method of checking the fuse or circuit breaker in the Operator's Manual.

   ---

5. Change the range to the next higher setting. Is the needle still setting on the zero (0) ohms?   *No*

   If not, readjust the zero-ohms setting.

6. Continue to do this for every range of the VOM.

   Discussion   Before the leads are connected, the needle does not deflect and is at or on top of the infinity symbol. This means that the resistance being measured is so **large** that no current is flowing through the meter movement—indicating that an open circuit might exist or that the range is too small for the resistor under test. It may be necessary to make the range selector greater to get any deflection.

When the leads are connected, the needle is at or on top of the zero. This indicates that the resistance is zero ohms or that the range being used is too large for the resistor under test. In this case the range selector will have to be changed to a lower setting in order to get a good indication of the resistance being measured.

The process of shorting the leads and making sure the needle is at or over the zero ohms setting is called "zeroing the meter."

Three very important rules will be repeated many times.

   a. Always remove power from the circuit before measuring any component with the ohmmeter.

   b. Always connect the ohmmeter leads across the component or resistor under test.

   c. When the range selector is changed always "zero the meter."

7. Set the controls of the VOM on the lowest ohms setting.

   Zero the meter on this scale.

8. Place the meter leads across the 10-kΩ resistor.

   What number is the needle at or over?

   ~~6.8KΩ~~ Infinite   10k

   Is the scale easy to interpret?   10kΩ X

9. Change the range until the needle deflects toward the middle of the scale.

   Disconnect the leads from one end of the resistor, connect the meter leads together, and zero the meter.

   ⚠ CAUTION   Each time you change ranges you must "zero the meter."

10. Connect the leads of the meter across the 10-kΩ resistor.

   Multiply the range selector and the meter indication.

   $$\underline{\quad 10 \quad} \times \underline{\quad 2,000 \quad} = \underline{\quad 10K \quad} \, \Omega$$

   (Meter Indication) × (Range Selector) = Resistor Value

11. Measure each resistor indicating the number from the scale and the range value. Then indicate the value of the resistor under test.

Scale indication		Range		Measured value
10 Ω	×	2,000 Ω	=	10K Ω
8.1 Ω	×	200 Ω	=	8.1 kΩ
1.48 kΩ	×	20 kΩ	=	1.5 kΩ
.550 Ω	×	2 kΩ	=	560 Ω
~~8.10 kΩ~~	20 MΩ	=	1 m Ω
200 kΩ	×	1000 Ω	=	100 kΩ
4.6 kΩ	×	20000 Ω	=	4.7 kΩ
		20 kΩ		

12. Determine if the resistors measured are within the stated tolerance.

Example In this example, assume the stated tolerance is 5%.

10 k ohms ±5%
10,000 × .05 = 500 Ω (amount of tolerance)
10,000 + 500 = 10,500 Ω (maximum value)
10,000 − 500 = 9,500 Ω (minimum value)

Enter the calculated minimum and maximum values, for each resistor in Table 5-1.

RESISTOR	MINIMUM VALUE	MAXIMUM VALUE
1-MΩ	1,050,000 Ω (1.05MΩ)	950 KΩ
100-kΩ	105,000 Ω / 105 KΩ	95 KΩ
10-kΩ	10,500 Ω / 10.5 KΩ	9.5 KΩ
8.2-kΩ	7.79 KΩ	8.61 KΩ
4.7-kΩ	4.465 KΩ	4.935 KΩ
1.5-kΩ	1.425 KΩ	1.575 KΩ
560-Ω	532 Ω	588 Ω

Table 5-1

If any resistor appears to be out of tolerance, measure the resistor again or recalculate the minimum and maximum tolerance values to be sure the resistor is out of tolerance.

13. Compare your answers with another lab team and state any observations made about the differences noted between the indicated values and the measured values.

Discussion Your observations should have included:

Some resistors are below the stated value, but within tolerance.

Some resistors are above the stated value, but within tolerance.

All of the resistors should have been in tolerance.

Observations

1. State the three important rules for measuring resistance with an ohmmeter.

   1) Always remove power from the circuit before using an ohmmeter
   2) Always connect the ohmmeter leads across the ~~computer~~ component or resistor under test

   3) When a range is selected always "zero the meter"

2. If a 5.6-kΩ ±5% resistor measures 5.9 kΩ, is it within tolerance?

   5800 Ω
   or
   5.8 kΩ

   No

   If you answered NO, by how much is it out of tolerance?

   100 Ω

3. If a 6.8-kΩ resistor with no tolerance band measures 5.7 kΩ, is it within tolerance?

   Yes, Minimum tolerance is
   5.44 kΩ

Variable Resistors

Name **Donivan J. Mc Greal** Class _____ Date **06/23/06**

Objectives	Upon completion of this experiment, you should be able to:
	• Recognize the basic characteristics of a variable resistor.
	• Connect a variable resistor as a rheostat.
	• Connect a variable resistor as a potentiometer.
Text Reference	Terrell, *Fundamentals of Electronics: DC/AC Circuits* Chapter 2, Section 2-7
Materials Required	2 Ohmmeters Variable Resistors: 1 kΩ 10 kΩ 20 kΩ 100 kΩ

Introduction

Variable resistors are available in all shapes and sizes. The physical size generally indicates the amount of power or heat the component can dissipate. Smaller variable resistors, or trim pots as they are called, have to be adjusted using a small common screwdriver or alignment tool. These are the types that will be used throughout this experiment and lab manual.

All variable resistors have the same type of construction. A connection is made at each end of the resistor and a floating or wiper arm connection is the center connection. The center connection can be at either end, in the middle, or anywhere in-between. Hence, the name variable resistor.

The amount of total resistance is generally indicated on the variable resistor. Some are coded to indicate this resistance.

Example	103 would indicate a 10,000-Ω variable resistor.
	The third number indicates the number of zeros to add to the first two numbers.
	If the number on the variable resistor is 502, write down the 50, then two additional zeros. This would indicate a 5000-ohm or 5-kΩ resistor.
	Others have the actual value printed on them: 1 kΩ, 20 kΩ, and so forth.

A bottom view of a typical variable resistor is shown in Figure 6-1. For this experiment we will number the pins or leads as shown.

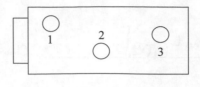

Figure 6-1

The total resistance can be measured between Pins 1 and 3. Pin 2 is the wiper arm or floating connection and is movable toward both ends of the resistor.

Procedures

1. Using the ohmmeter, measure the total resistance of each variable resistor between Pins 1 and 3. Then enter the measured value in Table 6-1.

RESISTOR	MEASURED VALUE
1-kΩ	937 ΩΩ
10-kΩ	10.39 K ΩΩ
20-kΩ	20.5 KΩΩ
100-kΩ	98.2 KΩΩ

Table 6-1

2. Connect the ohmmeter between Pins 1 and 2 of the 1-kΩ variable resistor. Refer to Figure 6-2.

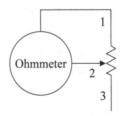

Figure 6-2

3. Adjust the variable resistor, turning the adjustment tool counterclockwise (CCW) and observing the indication on the ohmmeter.

4. Does the resistance increase or decrease as it is adjusted?

Yes

5. Adjust the variable resistor CCW until there is no longer a change in resistance.

6. Now adjust the variable resistor clockwise (CW), observing the ohmmeter indication.

7. Does the resistance increase or decrease as it is adjusted?

   Decreases

8. Repeat Steps 2 through 7 for the 10-kΩ, 20-kΩ, and 100-kΩ variable resistors.

9. State what happens to the resistance of each variable resistor as it is adjusted CCW.

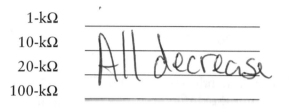

   1-kΩ   *resistance will stop at 1KΩ*
   10-kΩ   "   "   "   *at 10KΩ*   } *All increase*
   20-kΩ   "   "   "   *at 20KΩ*
   100-kΩ   "   "   "   *at 100KΩ*

10. State what happens to the resistance of each variable resistor as it is adjusted CW.

    1-kΩ   _____
    10-kΩ
    20-kΩ   *All decrease*
    100-kΩ   _____

11. Connect the 10-kΩ resistor as shown in Figure 6-3.

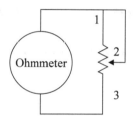

Figure 6-3

12. Place the ohmmeter across Pins 1 and 3.

13. State what you think will happen to the resistance value indicated by the ohmmeter when it is adjusted CCW. (Resistance will increase\decrease.)

    Increase

14. Adjust the resistor CCW and observe the ohmmeter. What happened to the resistance value between Pins 1 and 3?

    Decrease

Discussion   The variable resistor is connected as a rheostat, because the resistance between Pins 1 and 3 changes as the adjustment is made. The same results can be accomplished by connecting the ohmmeter between Pins 1 and 2. That is why it will be stated that a rheostat can be a two-pin connection. The configuration shown in Figure 6-3 is the one most commonly used in many schematic diagrams.

15. Connect the variable resistor, as shown in Figure 6-4, using both ohmmeters at the same time. Make sure that Ohmmeter #2 is connected to Pins 1 and 2.

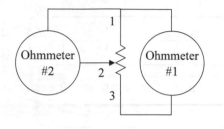

Figure 6-4

16. Adjust the variable resistor CW until the indication on Ohmmeter #2 no longer changes. State your observations about the differences between Ohmmeter #1's indication and Ohmmeters #2's indication.

Difference is about 5.10 KΩ differences

Resistance increases together

17. Slowly adjust the variable resistor CCW, observing both ohmmeters.

State what you observed about the resistance between Pins 1 and 2, as the variable resistor is adjusted fully CCW.

Decreases together

18. Change Ohmmeter #2 to measure the resistance between Pins 2 and 3.

Adjust the variable resistor slowly fully CW, then slowly adjust it CCW, observing the ohmmeter indications.

decreases CW
increases CCW

State what you observed about the resistance between Pins 2 and 3, as the variable resistor was adjusted fully CW then CCW.

Resistance increase to indicated value with possible tolerance consideration.

Decreases all the way to 0ohm

Discussion   This configuration is referred to as a potentiometer or pot. Its name will become apparent in later experiments.

The resistance between Pins 1 and 3 did not appear to change, but the resistance between Pins 1 and 2 changed as the variable resistor was adjusted. The resistance between Pins 2 and 3 also changed as the adjustments were made.

If the total resistance between Pins 1 and 3 appears to change, then the variable resistor is being used as a rheostat.

If the resistance between Pins 1 and 3 remains the same, but the resistance between the center wiper arm (Pin 2) and one end changes (either Pin 1 or 3), then the variable resistor is being used as a potentiometer.

Connecting Resistive Circuits

Name _Donivan Mc Creal_   Class _ET_   Date _06/30/06_

Objectives   Upon completion of this experiment, you should be able to:

- Use the protoboard.

- Construct basic resistive circuits.

- Determine if the circuits are connected correctly by using the ohmmeter.

Text Reference   Terrell, *Fundamentals of Electronics: DC/AC Circuits*
  Chapter 3, Section 3-2

Materials Required

Ohmmeter	6.8-kΩ resistor
20 or 22 gage connecting wire	8.2-kΩ resistor
1-kΩ resistor	Various test leads
2.2-kΩ resistor	Protoboard
3.3-kΩ resistor	

Introduction

Although the protoboard you may be using is larger than the one shown in Figure 7-1, how the board is connected should be very similar to yours.

When viewing the front of the board the holes that are in a vertical line from top to bottom (Column A on Figure 7-2) and down each side are connected together. When we view the back we can see that a continuous vertical connection exists. Therefore, if a hole is selected at the very top and you look straight down (vertically), they are connected electrically. When a larger board is used they may not be connected at the vertical center of the board.

The vertically connected holes are commonly referred to as the bus strip; the bus strip holes are normally used for power supply connections.

In the horizontal center of the board, there are multiple rows consisting of two sets of five horizontal holes. Each set of five horizontal holes is connected. Notice the back view and you can see that the sets of horizontal holes are not connected together. There are five holes which make a single electrical connection.

Inside each hole of the protoboard is a conductor that will make an electrical connection to the lead of a resistor or component inserted into the hole.

⚡CAUTION   **Do not insert a wire or a component lead with a gage value smaller than 18. This will damage the conductor inside the protoboard and will render this hole unusable.**

Further proof of the electrical connections are experimentally shown in the following procedures.

Front side top   Back side top

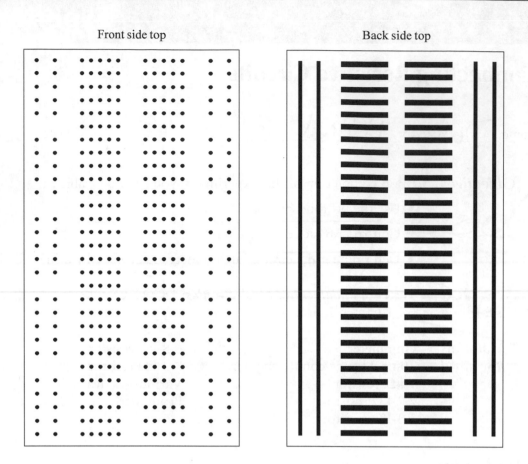

Figure 7-1 ProtoboardFigures

Procedures

1. Prepare two pieces of connecting wire, each about one to two inches in length, that are stripped on both ends.

   Connect each meter lead to a connecting wire. This will allow the wire and the meter leads to connect electrically to the holes when they are inserted into the holes of the protoboard.

2. Set the ohmmeter to the lowest ohms range.

3. Refer to Figure 7-2. Insert one of the meter leads into the topmost left side hole, marked Point 1.

   Insert the other meter lead into the bottommost left side hole, marked Point 2 in Figure 7-2.

4. What does the ohmmeter indicate about the connections between the two points?

Column A

Figure 7-2

Discussion   If the ohmmeter indicates zero ohms, they are connected; if the ohmmeter indicates infinite ohms, then the holes are not connected.

5. Move the bottom meter lead toward Point 1 to determine if the top hole is connected to the other vertical holes.

If the bottom hole is not connected to the top hole, find where the break in the connection occurs and connect a wire between these two points.

6. Repeat Steps 3 through 5 for the remaining bus strips on the protoboard.

7. Connect one lead of the ohmmeter to Point 3 and the other end of the meter to Point 4. State your observation.

    0 resistance

8. Leaving one end of the ohmmeter at Point 3, connect the other end of the meter to Point 5 and state your observation.

    0 resistance

9. Repeat Step 7 for Points 6 and 7. State your observations about how Points 3 through 7 are connected or not connected.

    0 resistance

10. Leaving one end of the meter connected to Point 3, connect the other end of the ohmmeter to Point 8 and state your observation.

    Infinite resistance

11. Are Points 8 through 12 connected?

    Yes

12. Are Points 13 and 14 connected?

    No

Discussion   Points 3 through 7 are connected and Points 8 through 12 are connected. However, Points 3 and 8 are not connected and neither are Points 13 and 14.

13. Connect a 1-kΩ resistor between Points 3 and 7.

14. Connect the ohmmeter across the 1-kΩ resistor and record the indicated value.
Indicated value ~~RB~~ ~~4B~~ *Ohms* Ω

State your observation about connecting the resistor between Points 3 and 7.

~~Clos~~ *the circuit between the 2 points*
Shorts

Discussion   The meter should have indicated zero ohms. This means that the resistor is **shorted** or the connection is causing the resistor to appear as a short. This can easily be checked by measuring the resistor when it is removed from the protoboard. However, having completed Steps 8 and 9 it is known that Points 3 and 7 are electrically connected together. Therefore, it appears that the resistor is shorted.

---

15. Connect the 1-kΩ resistor between Points 3 and 11 and measure the resistor with an ohmmeter, recording the value indicated by the ohmmeter.
Value indicated *990* Ω

Is this a normal reading for the 1-kΩ resistor?

Yes

Discussion   Your conclusion should be: do not connect resistors between points on the board that are electrically connected. When in doubt, check it with an ohmmeter before connecting a component between the two points.

Observe Figure 7-3 and note the connections for the entire protoboard. Notice the lines connecting the holes, both vertically and horizontally. This is how your protoboard is probably connected.

By observing Figure 7-4, you might find a way to connect the bus strips of the protoboard to more easily make power supply connections, regardless of what part of the board is used. This way the banana connections can be used to make direct connections to the board and the power supply. The supply voltage will be distributed throughout the entire board.

The next part of this experiment deals with basic circuit construction. The resistive circuits will be constructed on the protoboard, using the ohmmeter for verification of the correct circuit construction. Follow the procedures carefully using the figures shown. Then use the ohmmeter to verify circuit connections.

Compare the indicated ohmmeter values to the values given in the procedures to verify proper construction.

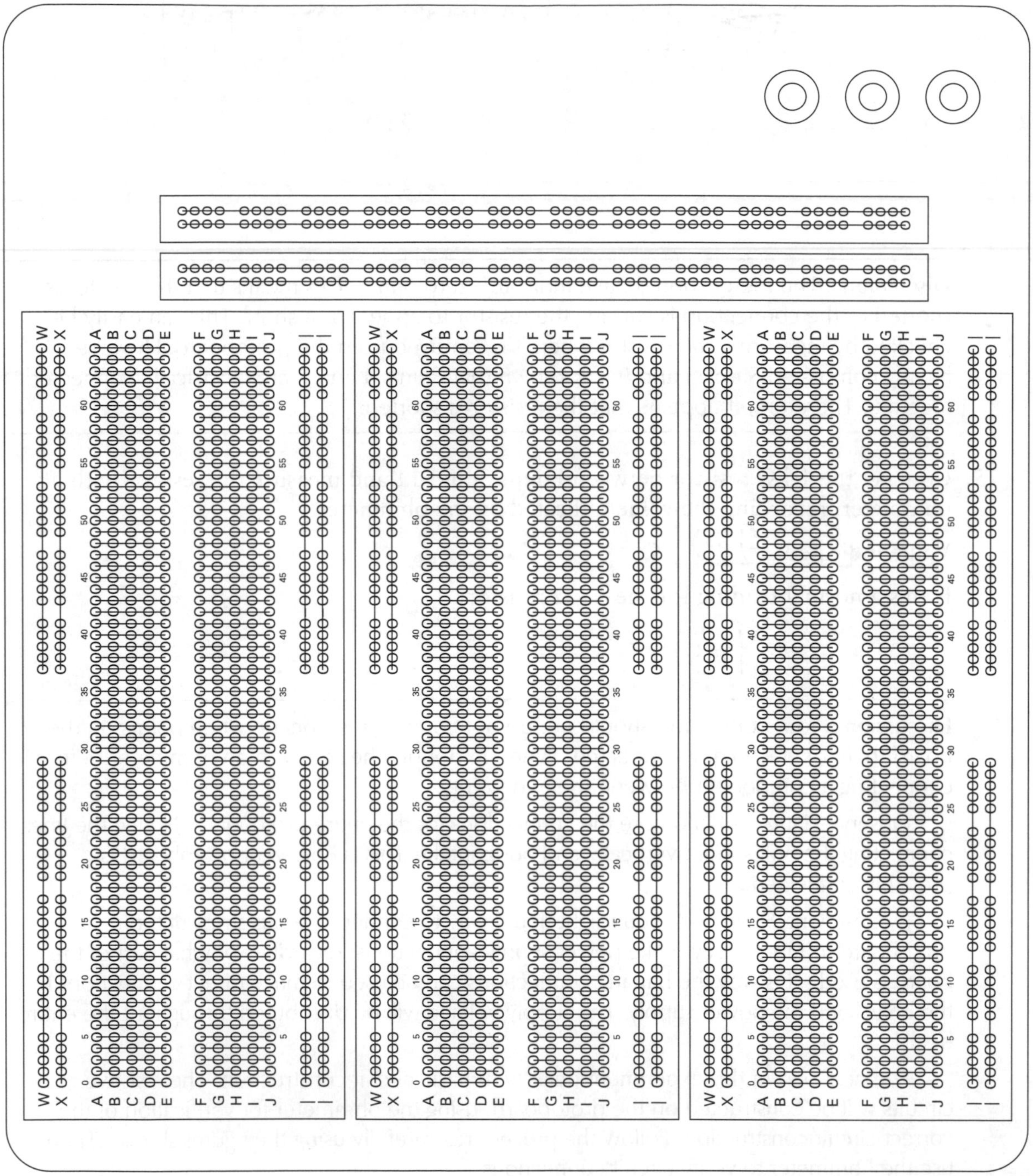

Figure 7-3

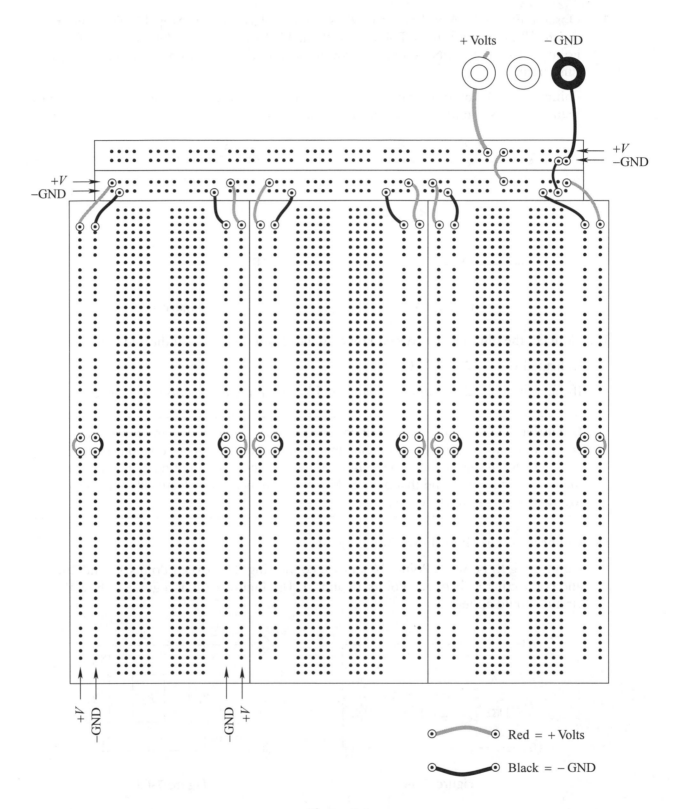

Figure 7-4

16. Observe Figure 7-5A and note that R_1 is connected as stated in Step 15. To connect resistor R_2, connect it from Point 12 to Point 15. Resistor R_3 can be connected from Point 14 to Point 13. Note Figure 7-5B. It includes the point to point connection for this circuit.

Points A and B would be between Points 3 and 13 as indicated in Figure 7-5B. Refer to Figure 7-5B as a guide to how the circuit should appear.

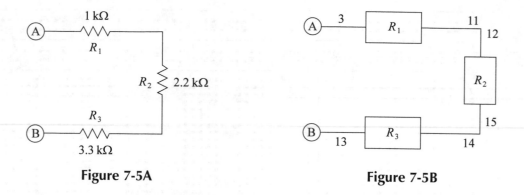

Figure 7-5A   **Figure 7-5B**

17. Connect the ohmmeter between Points A and B and record the indicated value.

Indicated value ___6.42K___ Ω

If the indicated value is approximately 6.5 kΩ, then the connections are correct.

Discussion   This is a series circuit. It has one path for current and all the resistors are connected end-to-end with no other component connected at their junction. The total resistance is the sum of the three resistors. Observe Figure 7-6A, noting that there is more than one current path and that both ends of all components are electrically connected together. This is a parallel circuit.

---

18. Connect the circuit as shown in Figure 7-6A by:

Connecting R_1 between Points 16 and 19, connecting R_2 between Points 17 and 20, and connecting R_3 between Points 18 and 21. Use Figure 7-6B as a guide to how the circuit should appear.

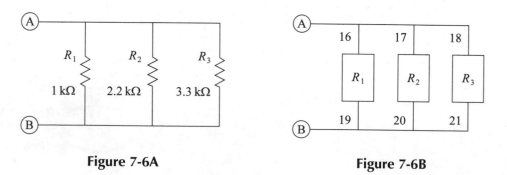

Figure 7-6A   **Figure 7-6B**

19. Points 16 and 19 are Points A and B as shown in Figure 7-6B. Connect the ohmmeter to Points A and B and record the indicated value.

Indicated value ___559___ Ω

If the indicated value is approximately 570 Ω, then the connections are as outlined in Step 19.

20. Observe Figure 7-7A. This is a combination of a series circuit and a parallel circuit.

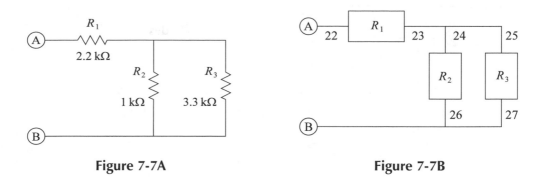

Figure 7-7A   Figure 7-7B

21. Construct the circuit as shown in Figure 7-7A by:

Connecting R_1 from Point 22 to Point 23, connecting R_2 from Point 24 to Point 26, and connecting R_3 from Point 25 to Point 27.

Figure 7-7B shows how the circuit should look on the protoboard as well as the point-to-point connections.

22. Points 22 and 27 are the same as Points A and B in Figure 7-7B.

Connect the ohmmeter between Points A and B and record the indicated value.

Indicated value _2.92K_ Ω

If the indicated value is approximately 3 kΩ, then the connections are as outlined in Step 22.

23. Construct the circuit as shown in Figure 7-8A.

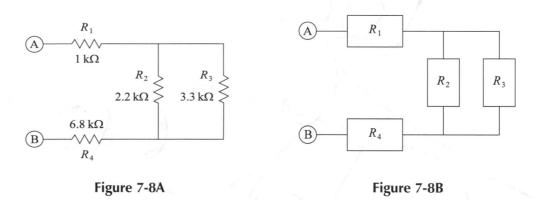

Figure 7-8A   Figure 7-8B

24. Measure the resistance between Points A and B and record the indicated value.

Indicated value _9.63kΩ_

If the indicated value is approximately 9.1 kΩ, then the connections are correct. Use Figure 7-8B as an aid when connecting this circuit.

25. Construct the circuit as shown in Figure 7-9A, using Figure 7-9B as an aid.

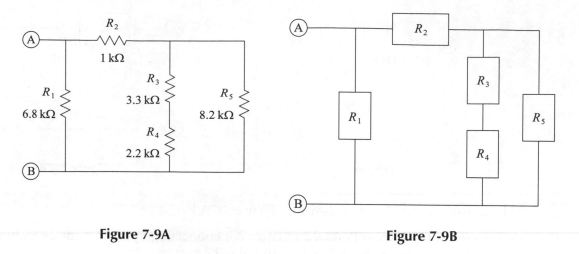

Figure 7-9A   **Figure 7-9B**

26. Measure the resistance between Points A and B and record the indicated value.

    Indicated value $2.85 K\Omega$

    The indicated value should be approximately 2.9 kΩ.

Discussion   Do not be concerned about how the indicated values were determined. If they come close to the given values, then the circuit is constructed correctly. At this point, correct construction is the objective. The why, will be a concern in later experiments.

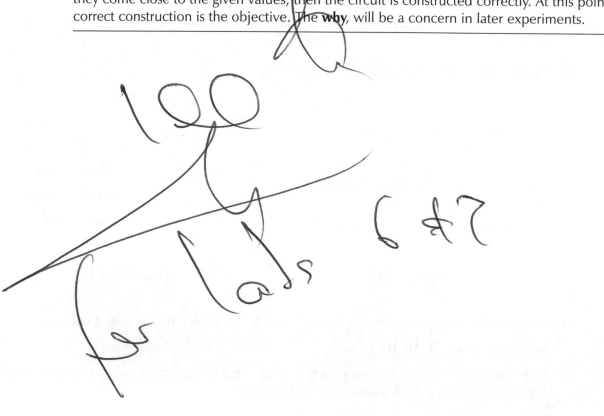

Current Meter; Ammeter

Name **Donivan McGreal**   Class _____   Date **06/30/06**

Objectives   Upon completion of this experiment, you should be able to:

- Insert the current meter in the circuit.
- Estimate the current value.
- Become proficient at reading the current meter.
- Observe the relationship between current and voltage.

Text Reference   Terrell, *Fundamentals of Electronics: DC/AC Circuits*
       Chapter 2, Section 2-3
       Chapter 9, Section 9-3

Materials Required   An analog current meter, a VOM, or a DMM capable of measuring 10 mA.
VOM or DMM for use as a voltmeter
Variable power supply; 0 to 20 volts dc
2.2-kΩ resistor
Various test leads

Introduction

A current meter, sometimes referred to as an ammeter, measures the current that flows through the meter at the point in the circuit where it is inserted.

Although the current meter is generally not practical in most real-world troubleshooting applications, it is important to understand how to use a current meter. It is more important to use the current meter in analysis of circuit operations than in everyday applications.

The most important thing to remember about the current meter is that it must be in-line with the circuit under test. In order to make it in-line with the component or circuit under test, first **break** the circuit. In order to break the circuit a **gap** must be created in the circuit. The current meter is inserted into this gap.

One of the more important uses for a current meter is in monitoring changes in current while other factors are varied. The factors that can be varied are voltage and resistance. By monitoring the changes in current, relationships can be established between these factors and current.

Procedures

1. Connect the power supply to the 2.2-kΩ resistor as shown in Figure 8-1.

   ⚠ CAUTION Do not turn on the power supply until directed to do so.

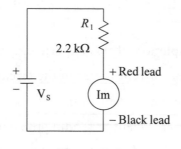

Figure 8-1

Discussion   It is always a good idea to turn off the power before inserting any current meter. Remember to trace current and connect the meter, always observing proper polarity. The current should enter the black jack and exit the red jack. Set the range of the current meter to the highest range and then decrease the range until a clear indication of the current can be observed.

---

2. Make sure the current meter controls are set for measuring current and that the proper input(s) are connected.

   Break the connection between the negative side of the power supply and the resistor.

3. Connect the common lead (black) of the current meter to the negative side of the power supply.

4. Connect the red lead of the current meter to the resistor.

Discussion   Consider current flow starting at the negative side of the power supply, through the meter, then through the resistor and back to the positive side of the power supply. A complete path for current exists. The same value of current will pass through the resistor and the meter; therefore, we can monitor the current through the resistor. Electron current flow will enter the meter at the common (black) lead and exit the positive (red) lead of the meter.

   If you are using a DMM, most are not polarity sensitive and the direction of current through the meter is not of importance. However, it is always a good practice to connect the meter as indicated in the above steps.

---

5. Disconnect the common lead (black) of the current meter from the negative side of the power supply.

6. Connect the voltmeter across the power supply.

7. Turn on the power supply and adjust the voltage control until the voltmeter indicates 2 volts.

8. **Turn off the power supply.**

   Remove the voltmeter from across the power supply and place it across the resistor.

   Discussion   Make sure the voltmeter is connected so that proper polarity is observed, even if you are using a DMM that is not sensitive to polarity. It is always good practice.

   ---

9. Reconnect the common lead (black) of the current meter to the negative side of the power supply.

10. Make sure the current meter range is at the highest range.

11. Turn on the power supply.

12. Record the current reading.

    909.05 μA

    I_m = ~~430 A~~ ~~435 A~~ ~~435 A~~

   Discussion   If using a DMM, decrease the range to get the most accurate reading— at least two decimal places. If using a VOM, try to keep the deflection in the center of the scale.

   Record the voltage across the resistor.

   V_R = 2 volts

13. Turn off the power supply and disconnect the current meter.

14. Connect the negative side of the power supply to the resistor.

15. Connect the current meter as shown in Figure 8-2.

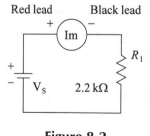

Figure 8-2

   Discussion   Remember to break the circuit and insert the current meter into the gap. Observe proper polarity. This means connecting the common lead of the current meter to the resistor and the red lead of the current meter to the positive side of the power supply.

   ---

16. Turn on the power supply and state your observations about the current value and the voltage across the resistor. Compare Steps 9 through 16 to write your observations.

How do the values compare? How many paths for current are there? Is there any voltage across the current meter (measurable)? *The values are the same.*

The current across the resistor is the same throughout the circuit
the voltage drop across the resistor is the same as the voltage applied
There was only one path for current to flow. Yes, the voltage across
the resistor was the same as the voltage applied

Discussion   If a circuit has only one current path, it does not matter where the current is measured. The current meter has a very small voltage drop.

These are observations that should be noted at this time. They will become very important as you progress through the next several experiments.

---

17. **Turn off the power supply.** Set the controls of the current meter to measure at least 10 mA.

18. Turn on the power supply and slowly adjust it until there are 5 volts across the resistor.

19. When the voltage across the resistor was increased, what happened to the current through the resistor and current meter? If necessary adjust the power supply until the voltage across the resistor is 0 V and slowly adjust until the voltage across the resistor is again 5 volts, observing the current meter indication.
    As voltage was increased the current measurement ~~increased~~ increased

20. Adjust the power supply until the current meter indicates 3 mA.

    What is the value of the resistor voltage drop?

    5 volts

    Does this support your answer in Step 19? Explain.

Discussion   If your answer to the above question was yes, then your explanation should have indicated that as current through the resistor increased the voltage across the resistor increased. This establishes the relationship between current and voltage. They are proportional values; meaning that as one increases the other should also increase.

---

21. To determine the value of current that will be measured when the power supply voltage is adjusted to 10 volts, the following steps should be used.

$$\frac{V_{Applied}}{R_{Total}} = I_{Total}$$

$$\frac{10 \text{ V}}{2.2 \text{ k}\Omega} = 4.5 \text{ mA}$$

Is the current meter set on the proper range to measure the estimated value of 4.5 mA?

22. Adjust the power supply until 10 volts is across the resistor.

How does the measured value compare with the estimated value?

The results were the same

23. **Turn off the power supply.** Remove the current meter from the circuit and connect the positive side of the power supply to the resistor.

24. Turn on the power supply.

The voltage across the resistor is now ___*10*___ volts.

25. Using the measured value of voltage determine the current through the resistor.

$$\frac{V_{Applied}}{R_{Total}} = I_{Total}$$

___*10*___ V ÷ 2.2 k = ___*4.54*___ mA

Is the voltage across the resistor the same value obtained in Step 21?

Somewhat, a slight difference of about .25 volts

Determine the difference between the two readings, if any.

About .25 volts

How does this value compare with the measured value of current?

Current was also affected by .005 mA

Discussion   Although the difference between the voltage readings obtained in Steps 22 and 23 should have been very small, there might have been a noticeable difference. Therefore, we can conclude that inserting a current meter **slightly** changes the normal circuit operations.

The difference noted or the difference that was too small to be observable, might be due to the type of meter used in the experiment. The differences might be so small that the type of meter used cannot measure the change. If this happens, do not be too concerned.

Estimating the current is important, because making sure the selected range is not exceeded is important to the health of the meter.

Some DMMs have auto-ranging—the meter automatically adjusts the range as needed. Therefore, the range would not be exceeded, but we need to have an idea of what is and is not a correct current value.

Observations

1. What factors affect the value of current?

   The type a value of the resistor
   How much voltage is applied

2. State two reasons for estimating or calculating the value of current.

   Estimate current to establish the proper procedure
   To create a hypothesis a answer In a virtual sense without
   damaging anything.

Ohm's Law

Name _Donovan Mc Greal_   Class _____   Date _06/30/06_

Objectives   Upon completion of this experiment, you should be able to:

- Observe that the current is inversely proportional to resistance.

- Observe that voltage and current are proportional.

- Observe that voltage and resistance are proportional.

Text Reference   Terrell, *Fundamentals of Electronics: DC/AC Circuits*
        Chapter 2, Section 2-6
        Chapter 3, Section 3-4

Materials Required   VOM or DMM for current meter
VOM or DMM for voltmeter and/or ohmmeter
Variable power supply 0 V to 20 V dc
1-kΩ resistor
2.2-kΩ resistor
5.6-kΩ resistor
8.2-kΩ resistor
10-kΩ resistor
Various test leads

Introduction

Ohmmeter   **When using an ohmmeter in a circuit, always remove power.** When using an ohmmeter to measure resistance, place the ohmmeter across the component.

When measuring a single component that is in a circuit, one lead or leg of the component must be free of the circuit. This will ensure an accurate measurement.

Current meter   When measuring current, the current meter must be connected in line or in series. Therefore, **break** the current path, cause a gap to appear, and insert the meter into the **gap**. Remember that current flows through a component. Therefore, current must flow into the current meter and through the current meter and out of the current meter.

Break the current path and insert the current meter into the created gap in the circuit.

When faced with a new circuit, trace current flow. Always start at the most negative point and go toward the most positive point of the circuit. As current is traced, indicate the polarity across each component that the current flows through. When you break the circuit, note which end of the circuit is closest to the negative terminal of the power supply and connect the black lead or common input lead to this point.

Most Digital Multimeters are not polarity sensitive. However, it is a good idea to practice observing polarity.

Equations   The following equations are variations of Ohm's Law.

$$V = I \times R \qquad I = \frac{V}{R} \qquad R = \frac{V}{I}$$

This experiment will provide information to verify each of the equations listed. By drawing the graphs relationships between the variables will be visualized. Draw the graphs carefully and observe what is indicated by each graph. Prove each relationship by referring back to the equations. Ask what happens to other values as one value increases or deceases. Remember to keep one value constant and change one value, then determine what happens to the third value.

Example   Suppose Current (*I*) increases and Resistance (*R*) remains the same, what happens to the voltage?

Because $V = I \times R$ and *I* increased, the voltage would also increase. This can be visualized by observing the graph of *V* versus *I*.

Important points to remember:

- Trace current first.
- Calculate current before measuring to ensure meter safety.
- Observe polarity for the voltmeter and current meter.
- The voltmeter is connected across the component.
- The current meter is connected in-line with the component.
- The ohmmeter is **never** used with power applied.

Indicate the polarity of the voltage across the resistor in Figure 9-1.

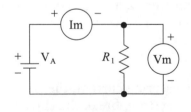

Figure 9-1

Voltmeter   The voltmeter, like the ohmmeter, must be placed across or in parallel with the component being measured. Think of the voltmeter as a rather large resistor which must have current flowing through it in order to indicate the amount of voltage.

Note Figure 9-1 and the meter marked Vm. This meter is across R_1 and has a current through it. Start at the negative terminal of the power supply and go through the voltmeter back to the positive side of the power supply, ignoring R_1 for an instant in time.

The voltmeter must be across the component being measured.

Procedures

1. Using an ohmmeter, measure the actual values of the resistors and record their values in Table 9-1.

RESISTOR VALUE	
1-kΩ	.97 kΩ or 970 Ω
2.2-kΩ	2.17 kΩ
5.6-kΩ	5.53 kΩ
8.2-kΩ	8.10 kΩ
10-kΩ	9.92 kΩ

Table 9-1

2. Using the voltmeter, place the leads of the voltmeter across the power supply terminals. Turn on the power supply and adjust the supply voltage for a meter indication of 6 volts. Then turn off the power supply.

   If the power supply has a metering device for indicating voltage, do not depend on this meter for accuracy. Always use the same meter when measuring voltage.

3. Connect the circuit as shown in Figure 9-2, using a 1-kΩ resistor for R_1.

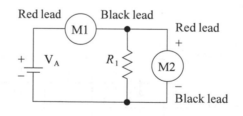

Figure 9-2

⚡ **CAUTION** Do not turn on the power supply until instructed to do so.

Is the current meter (M1) correctly installed and/or in-line to measure the correct polarity?

Yes

Is the voltmeter (M2) **across** the 1-kΩ resistor?

Yes

4. To determine or calculate the value of current through the circuit, divide the applied voltage of 6 volts by actual value of the 1-kΩ (1×10^3) resistor.

6 mA

Make sure that the current meter range setting is at the highest range setting. Then decrease the range setting until an accurate measurement can be made.

5. Turn on the power supply and record the voltage across R_1 and the current through the circuit.

M2 = V_{R_1} =   _____ 6 volts _____ volts

M1 = I_T =   _____ 4 mA. _____ milliamps

Does the measured value approximate the value determined in Step 4?

Discussion   Sometimes it is easier to determine results by drawing a graph of one variable versus another variable. The graph could be a summary of results observed as something is changed. In the next set of procedures the resistor value is going to change and the voltage will remain constant. The current will then be monitored for changes.

Observe Graph 9-1 and notice that resistance is the horizontal axis or X-axis and that current is the vertical axis or Y-axis. Follow the X-axis until 1 kΩ is located. Draw a vertical line that intersects this point. Then go vertically until the amount of measured current is located on the vertical axis. Draw a horizontal line that will intersect this current point. The point at where these lines meet place a dot. Now the vertical line and the horizontal line can be erased.

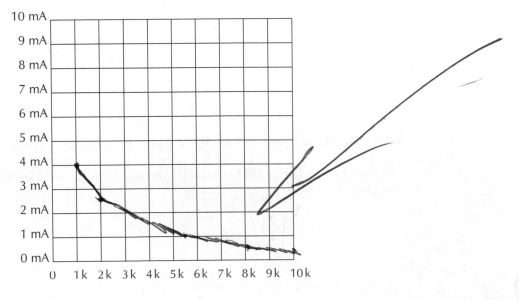

Graph 9-1

Notice that the values of resistors measured in Table 9-1 are along the horizontal axis. For each resistor the current value will be indicated by the meter when these resistors are placed in the circuit. Using the same basic procedure for each resistor, a graph can be created by connecting all of the dots.

6. **Turn off the power supply.** Remove the 1-kΩ resistor and replace it with a 2.2 kΩ resistor.

Calculate the value of current, to make sure the current range scale of the current meter will not be exceeded.

2. 7mA

Turn on the power supply.

7. Measure the current and place a dot on Graph 9-1 that corresponds to the value of current measured using the 2.2-kΩ resistor.

Discussion   The 2-kΩ line is apparent, but the value used was 2.2 kΩ. Use what point you think is 2.2 kΩ.

8. Repeat Steps 6 and 7 for the remainder of the resistors listed in Table 9-1. (Don't forget to calculate the value of current before measuring it.)

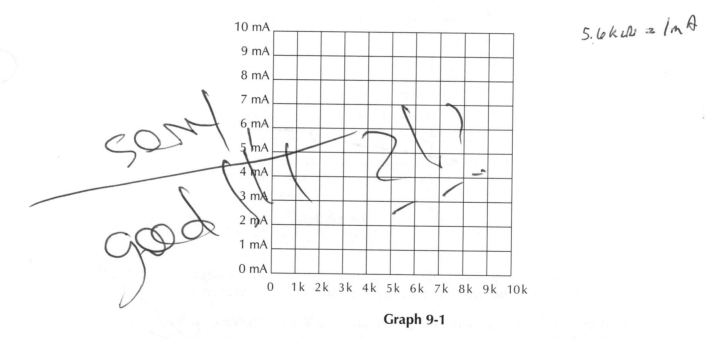

5.6kΩ = 1mA

Graph 9-1

9. Draw a smooth line to connect the points plotted on Graph 9-1. Then state your observations about what happens to the circuit current as the resistance is increased.

Discussion   Did you note that as the resistance increased, the current decreased? Therefore, current and resistance are inversely proportional; as one value goes up the other value goes down.

In the next set of procedures a graph of voltage versus current will be determined, with the resistance held constant. Using this graph, the relationship between voltage and current can be observed.

10. **Turn off the power supply,** remove the 10-kΩ resistor, and replace it with the 5.6-kΩ resistor.

    Place the voltmeter across R_1.

11. Turn on the power supply and adjust for a measurement of 1 volt across R_1.

12. On Graph 9-2, place a dot at the point that corresponds to the amount of current indicated by the current meter (M2) at 1 volt.

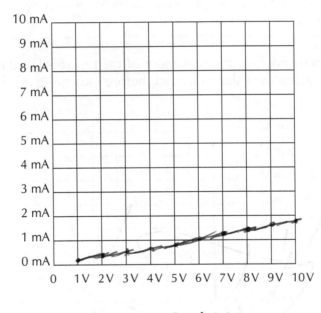

Graph 9-2

13. Slowly adjust the power supply voltage to 2 volts and place a dot on Graph 9-2 that corresponds to the amount of current indicated by the current meter (M2).

14. Repeat Step 13, increasing the power supply at 1-volt intervals, until the voltage across R_1 is 10 volts.

    Note   Remember to determine the value of current before adjusting for an increase in voltage. Then adjust the controls of the current meter to a range that will not be exceeded by the circuit current.

15. Draw a smooth line that connects all the dots you have placed on Graph 9-2.

State your observations, using Graph 9-2 as the reference.

The current increased with the voltage

Discussion   Notice that as you increased the voltage, the current increased even though the resistance remained constant. This indicates that voltage and current are proportional values.

---

16. **Turn off the power supply.**

Remove the 5.6-kΩ resistor and replace it with the 1-kΩ resistor, placing the voltmeter across resistor R_1.

17. Turn the power supply voltage adjustment to minimum.

Turn on the power supply and adjust it until a current of 1 mA is indicated by the current meter (M2).

18. Record the voltage across the resistor by placing a dot on Graph 9-3 at the point that corresponds to the voltage indicated by the voltmeter across the 1-kΩ resistor.

19. **Turn the power supply off** and remove the 1-kΩ resistor and replace it with the 2.2-kΩ resistor.

20. Turn the power supply voltage adjustment to minimum.

Turn on the power supply and adjust it until a current of 1 mA is indicated by the current meter (M2).

21. Record the voltage across resistor R_1 by placing a dot on Graph 9-3 at the point that corresponds to the voltage indicated by the voltmeter (M1).

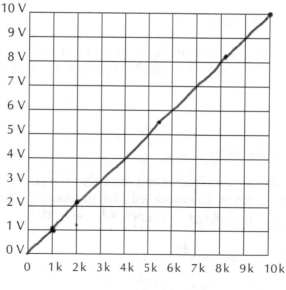

Graph 9-3

22. Repeat Steps 19, 20, and 21 for all the resistors listed in Table 9-1.

> **Note**   Remember to adjust the power supply for a 1 mA current indication before recording the voltage across the resistor on the graph.

23. Draw a smooth line that connects all the dots you have placed on Graph 9-3.

    State your observations concerning Graph 9-3.

    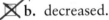 as the resistance increased increased, voltage needed to be raised to keep the current 1mA

Discussion   Notice that as the resistor was increased in value, the power supply voltage had to be adjusted to a higher value in order to maintain a constant current of 1 mA. This demonstrates that resistance and voltage are proportional values.

Observations

1. When troubleshooting a circuit, the current is too high even though the power supply voltage has not changed. This indicates that the resistance has

   ☐ a. increased.

   ☒ b. decreased.

   ☐ c. remained the same.

2. The voltage across a fixed resistor is too high in a given circuit. This indicates that the circuit current has

   ☒ a. increased.

   ☐ b. decreased.

   ☐ c. remained the same.

3. When troubleshooting a circuit you notice that the circuit current is correct, but the voltage across a resistor is too high. This indicates that the resistance has

   ☐ a. increased.

   ☒ b. decreased.

   ☐ c. remained the same.

4. When troubleshooting a circuit you notice that the circuit current is too high and the resistor measures within tolerance with an ohmmeter. What is the problem?

   Too much voltage is applied to the circuit

5. State two reasons the circuit current could decrease, proving your answers with the equations stated in the experiment.

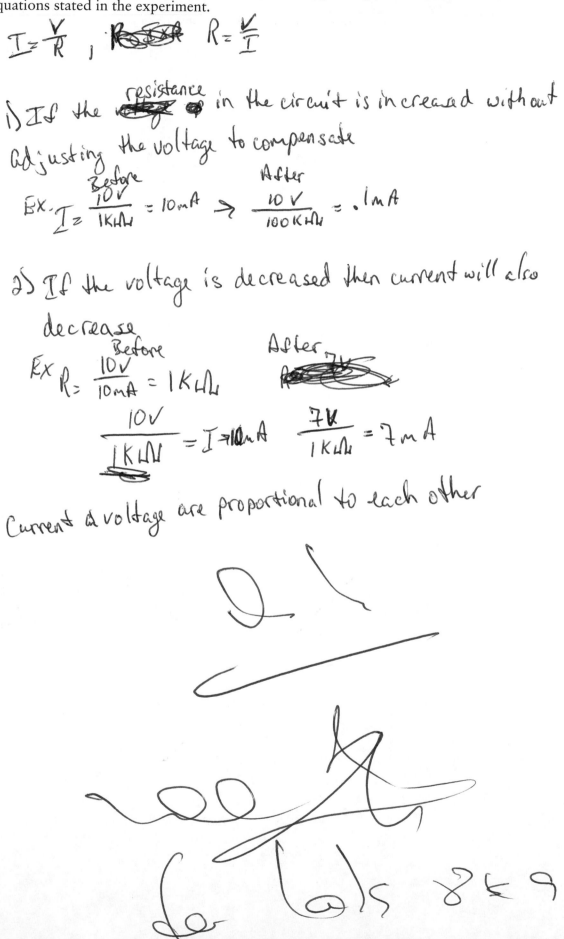

$$I = \frac{V}{R} \quad , \quad \cancel{R = V \cdot R} \quad R = \frac{V}{I}$$

1) If the ~~voltage~~ resistance in the circuit is increased without adjusting the voltage to compensate

$$\text{EX.} \quad I = \frac{\overset{\text{Before}}{10V}}{1K\Omega} = 10mA \quad \rightarrow \quad \frac{\overset{\text{After}}{10V}}{100K\Omega} = .1mA$$

2) If the voltage is decreased then current will also decrease

$$\text{EX} \quad R = \frac{\overset{\text{Before}}{10V}}{10mA} = 1K\Omega \qquad \overset{\text{After}}{\cancel{}}$$

$$\frac{10V}{1K\Omega} = I = 10mA \qquad \frac{7V}{1K\Omega} = 7mA$$

Current & voltage are proportional to each other

Series Resistive Circuits: Level I

Name _Donovan McPhee_   Class _DC Electronics_ Date _07/7/06_

Objectives   Upon completion of this experiment, you should be able to:

- Observe that the total resistance is equal to the sum of all the resistors in the series circuit.

- Observe that the sum of the voltage drops across each resistor is equal to the applied voltage.

- Observe that the total circuit current is equal to the current through each resistor **or** the current value is the same at any point in the circuit.

Text Reference   Terrell, *Fundamentals of Electronics: DC/AC Circuits*
      Chapter 4, Sections 4-1 through 4-4

Materials Required   Current meter
Voltmeter
Ohmmeter
Variable power supply; 0 to 20 volts dc
1-kΩ resistor
470-Ω resistor
330-Ω resistor
Various test leads

Introduction

Review the objectives to make sure the concepts listed are familiar. If any of the concepts are not familiar, review these concepts in Chapter 4 of the Terrell text.

In addition, the following concepts were covered in previous labs; ensure they are understood:

- Use of the current meter, voltmeter, and ohmmeter

- Series circuit construction

- Use of the variable power supply

If not, review the previous labs.

Read all the procedures of the lab before actually performing the steps. As you are reading the steps try to visualize what the result will be (determine or calculate the values). Write down notes to indicate "What you think the result will be." When actually performing the step(s), compare the experimental results to the expected results.

Procedures

1. Use the ohmmeter to measure the value of each of the selected resistors. List the values in the spaces provided in Table 10-1.

RESISTOR VALUES	
1-kΩ	977 Ω
470-Ω	461 Ω
330-Ω	325 Ω

Table 10-1

2. Construct the circuit as shown in Figure 10-1.

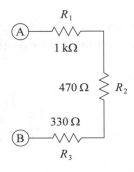

Figure 10-1

3. Place the ohmmeter between points A and B and measure the total resistance of the circuit.

   Ohmmeter indication ___1.76 KΩ___ Ω

4. Using the data collected in Table 10-1, determine the sum of the three resistors.

   Sum of the resistors ___1.76 KΩ___ Ω

5. In your own words, state your observation concerning the two values obtained in Steps 3 and 4.

   The 2 values are equal. The sum of the three resistors are proportional to each individual component resistance.

Discussion   The two values should be within 5 to 10% of each other, although you may have slight variances which could be due to parallax, accuracy of the meter reading, and so forth.

The answers should be very close to 1.8 kΩ. This proves that the sum of all the resistors in a series circuit is equal to the total resistance of the circuit.

---

6. Turn the voltage adjustment for the variable power supply to minimum.

   Connect the variable power supply to Points A and B as shown in Figure 10-2.

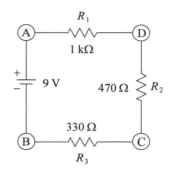

Figure 10-2

7. Connect the voltmeter to Points A and B and adjust the power supply for 9 volts. Make sure that the red lead of the voltmeter is connected to Point A and the common or black lead is connected to Point B.

8. Record the indicated value of the voltmeter in the appropriate space for each resistor in Table 10-2, measuring the voltage across each resistor by placing the voltmeter leads as follows:

   V_{R_1} Place the red lead at Point D and the common or black lead at Point A.

   V_{R_2} Place the red lead at Point C and the common or black lead at Point D.

   V_{R_3} Place the red lead at Point B and the common or black lead at Point C.

VOLTAGES VALUES	
V_{R_1}	−4.98
V_{R_2}	−2.35
V_{R_3}	~1.66
V_{Total}	+9 V

Table 10-2

Discussion   Note that each of the measured values is negative. Draw the current path in the circuit and indicate the polarity of the voltage across each resistor. Note that each time you measured the component voltage, the red lead was placed on the negative side of the resistor.

---

9. Determine the sum of the measured values recorded in Table 10-2.

   Sum of voltages across the resistors __-8.99__ volts

Discussion   The sum of the resistor voltages should equal negative 9 volts, or very close. This indicates that when the supply voltage is added to the **voltage drops** the algebraic sum is **zero**; the sum of the voltage drops is equal to the applied voltage.

---

10. **Turn off the power supply. Break** the circuit at Point A.

    Insert the current meter, in series or in-line, between the two ends of Point A.

Discussion   Before you turn on the power, estimate the value of current in the circuit:

$$\frac{V_{Total}}{R_{Total}} = I_{Total}$$

$$\frac{9\,V}{1800\,\Omega} =$$

This will ensure that the range selected for the current meter will not be exceeded. Always set the current meter one range higher than the estimated value.

The meter range should be __5mA__ , to measure the circuit current in Figure 10-2.

---

11. Turn the power supply on and record the current value in the space provided in Table 10-3.

12. **Turn off the power supply,** disconnect the meter, and reconnect the circuit at Point A.

13. **Break** the circuit at Point B and insert the current meter into the circuit.

    Turn on the power supply and measure the current, recording the value in the space provided in Table 10-3.

14. State, in your own words, your observations about the currents measured at Point A and Point B.

15. Repeat Steps 12 and 13 for Points C and D.

CURRENT VALUES	
Current at Point A	5.1 mA
Current at Point B	5.1 mA
Current at Point C	5.1 mA
Current at Point D	5.1 mA

Table 10-3

16. Are all of the current values the same?

Yes

What does this indicate about the current in a series circuit?

Current remains the same throughout a series circuit

Observations

1. State the three characteristics of a series circuit that have been observed.

1) Total Resistance in a series circuit is added by each resistor value

2) Voltage Drop across each resistor is the difference of the total voltage - the 1st voltage drop measurement

3) Current increases as voltage increases. Resistance increase so does the voltage. As resistance increases, current decreases

2. If one of the resistors in Figure 10-3 has 6 volts across it and 2 milliamps of current through it, determine the size of the other resistor and the total resistance.

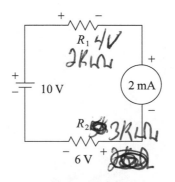

Figure 10-3

3. What characteristic(s) of a series circuit was/were used to solve the problem stated in
   Question 2.

   The voltage drops across the one resistor - minus
   the total voltage equals the voltage drop across R_1
   Taking the voltage drop across R_1 & R_2 divided by the
   current of 2mA equals the resistance of each resistor.

4. Draw a 4 resistor series circuit that has two 1-kΩ resistors, one 5-kΩ resistor, and a
   fourth unknown resistor. The total circuit resistance is 12.2 kΩ and the current
   flowing through the 5-kΩ resistor is 1.5 milliamps. Determine the value of the fourth
   unknown resistor, total circuit current, and the supply voltage value.

$R_T = 12.2k\Omega$

$R_4 = 5.2k\Omega$

$I_T = 1.5mA$

$V_T = 18.3 volts$

Series Circuits: Level II

Name _Donivan McGreal_ _____ Class_____ Date _____

Objectives	Upon completion of this experiment, you should be able to:

- Recognize the characteristics of series circuits as changes occur to the total resistance, by changing the value of one resistor.

- Recognize the changes in the circuit current, as one resistor is changed in value.

- Observe the voltage drops across each resistor, as one resistor is changed in value.

Text Reference	Terrell, *Fundamentals of Electronics: DC/AC Circuits* Chapter 4, Sections 4-1 through 4-4

Materials Required	VOM or DMM Variable power supply; 0 to 20 volts dc 5-kΩ variable resistor 1-kΩ resistor 2.2-kΩ resistor 3.3-kΩ resistor Various test leads

Introduction

In the previous experiment for series circuits the observations proved the following:

1. Current is the same throughout the circuit.

2. The sum of the voltage drops is equal to the applied voltage.

3. The sum of the resistors is equal to the total resistance.

In this experiment further investigation will result in the development of methods used to troubleshoot series circuits and further analyze them. Factors for investigation deal with changes in resistor values resulting in other circuit characteristics changing. Changes in the applied voltage cause variations in circuit current as well as in resistor voltage drops. Understanding how these factors cause changes in the circuit is the first step toward developing effective troubleshooting skills.

Read all the procedures of the lab before actually performing the steps. As you are reading the steps try to visualize what the result will be (estimate the values). Write down notes to indicate "What you think the result will be". When actually performing the steps, compare the actual results to the expected results.

After completing the lab, compare results with other lab teams and discuss differences between the observed results. In some cases it may be necessary to remeasure certain values to reenforce what has been learned.

Procedures

1. Use the ohmmeter to measure the actual value of each of the selected resistors. List the values in the provided spaces of Table 11-1. Then use the values listed in Table 11-1 to determine other circuit values, not the stated values. This will lead to fewer differences between expected and measured values.

RESISTOR VALUES	
1 kΩ	
2.2 kΩ	
3.3 kΩ	

Table 11-1

2. Connect the ohmmeter to the 1st and 2nd pins of the variable resistor shown in Figure 11-1.

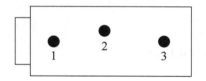

Figure 11-1   Variable resistor (Bottom view)

3. Adjust the variable resistor counterclockwise (CCW) or to the left and state whether the resistance is increasing or decreasing.

CCW and the resistance _____

4. Now adjust the variable resistor clockwise (CW) or to the right and state what happens to the resistance.

CW and the resistance _____

Discussion   When making adjustments to the variable resistor, refer to these steps to determine whether the resistance is being increased or decreased by the adjustment.

5. Adjust the variable resistor for 2.5 kΩ between the 1st and 2nd pins, to be used in Figure 11-2.

6. Construct the circuit as shown in Figure 11-2, making sure that Pins 1 and 2 of the variable resistor are used as R_4.

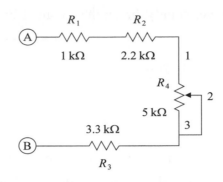

Figure 11-2

7. Determine the total resistance using the actual values listed in Table 11-1.

   Expected reading _____ Ω

   Place an ohmmeter between Points A and B and measure the total resistance of the circuit.

   Actual reading _____ Ω

8. Adjust the variable resistor CCW and state your observations.

   Review Step 2 and make sure your statement includes the information gained performing this step. Does the variable resistor cause an increase or decrease in the total circuit resistance?

9. Remove the variable resistor from the circuit. Readjust the variable resistor to 2.5 kΩ and reinsert it into the circuit.

10. Adjust the variable resistor CW and state your observations.

Discussion   Changing the value of a single resistor in a series circuit will cause an increase in the total resistance. If the change in a resistor increases, the total resistance increases; conversely, if the resistor decreases in value, the total resistance will decrease. This is an important first step in troubleshooting circuits.

---

11. Remove the variable resistor from the circuit and readjust it for 2.5 kΩ. Reinsert it into the circuit.

   Place a voltmeter between Points A and B. Connect the dc power supply between Points A and B and adjust it for 18 volts. (Use the voltmeter as the reference.)

12. **Turn off the power supply,** break the circuit at Point A, and insert a current meter into break of the circuit.

13. What current value do you expect the meter to indicate?

$$(I_T = ?)$$

Expected current _____ mA

14. Make sure the current meter range is higher than the expected current.

Turn on the power supply and record the actual circuit current.

Actual current _____ mA

15. If the value of one of the resistors increased, the total resistance would _____.

This means that the total current in the circuit would _____.

16. Prove your answers by adjusting the variable resistor in the direction that causes the resistance to increase.

State your observations about the circuit current, ensuring that the change in the resistance value is included. (If necessary turn off the power supply, remove the variable resistor, and measure it with the ohmmeter to make sure that the value increased).

17. If the variable resistor decreases in value, the total resistance will _____, which will cause a/an _____ in circuit current.

18. Prove your answers by adjusting the variable resistor in the direction that causes the resistance to decrease.

State your observations about the circuit current, ensuring that the change in the resistance value is included. (If necessary turn off the power supply, remove the variable resistor, and measure it with the ohmmeter to make sure that the value decreased to below 2.5 kΩ.)

19. **Turn off the power supply,** remove the variable resistor, and readjust the variable resistor to 2.5 kΩ.

    Reinsert the variable resistor and turn on the power supply.

20. Measure the voltage across each resistor and record the values in the provided spaces in the center column of Table 11-2.

VOLTAGE VALUES			
	When R_4 is 1 kΩ	When R_4 is 2.5 kΩ	When R_4 is 4 kΩ
V_{R_1}			
V_{R_2}			
V_{R_3}			
V_{R_4}			

Table 11-2

21. **Turn off the power supply,** remove the variable resistor, and adjust the rheostat for 1 kΩ.

22. Reinsert the variable resistor and turn on the power supply.

23. Measure the voltage across each resistor and record the value in the provided spaces on the left side of Table 11-2.

24. Observe the recorded voltage drops in Table 11-2 and state the reason differences occurred in the measurements. (Your statement should include changes in total resistance and changes in circuit current).

___

Discussion   When the variable resistor value is decreased to 1 kΩ the total circuit resistance decreases, causing an increase in circuit current. (Remember, the power supply voltage never changed). The voltage across R_1, R_2, and R_3 increased in value, while the voltage across R_4 decreased in value.

___

25. Determine the change in voltage across each resistor.

___

Example   Suppose that when the variable resistor was 2.5 kΩ, the voltage across R_1 was 6 volts. When the variable resistor was decreased, the voltage across R_1 went to 6.5 volts. Therefore, a 0.5 volt change occurred.

V_{R_1} changed by _____ volts

V_{R_2} changed by _____ volts

V_{R_3} changed by _____ volts

V_{R_4} changed by _____ volts

26. Add the changes in voltage of V_{R_1}, V_{R_2}, and V_{R_3}.

Sum of the increase of the voltage drops

_____ volts

Discussion   Note that the total increase in the voltage drops across R_1, R_2, and R_3 approximates the decrease in the voltage across R_4. This supports Kirchhoff's Voltage Law. If the power supply voltage remained constant and one voltage drop increased, then there must have been a voltage drop that decreased by the same amount. If a voltage drop increased in value, then the circuit current must have increased. This means that a decrease in total resistance occurred.

27. **Turn off the power supply,** remove the variable resistor, and adjust the variable resistor for 4 kΩ. Reinsert the resistor.

28. State in your own words what you expect will happen to the total circuit resistance, the circuit current, and each of the voltage drops in the circuit.

29. Turn on the power supply. Measure each voltage drop and record each value in the space provided on the right side of Table 11-2.

30. Compare your answer in Step 28 to the actual results of Step 29. Did the expected results closely match the actual results?

Discussion   When the variable resistor was made larger the total resistance increased and that caused a decrease in circuit current. Therefore, the voltage drops decreased, except for R_4. The voltage across R_4 increased by the same amount as the sum of the decreases in voltage drops across R_1, R_2, and R_3. If this did not occur, recheck your actual results.

Observations

1. Using the following words, fill in the blanks. (The words may be used as many times as needed.)

   a. sum

   b. total resistance

   c. increase(s)

   d. decrease(s)

   The total resistance is determined by the _____ of all the resistors in a closed loop. The circuit current is equal to the sum of the voltages across each resistor in a closed loop, divided by the _____. If one resistor _____ in value, the total resistance will increase and the circuit current will _____. The voltage drop across each resistor will _____, except for the resistor that increased in value. The voltage drop across the resistor that increased in value will _____. If one resistor decreases in value, the total resistance will _____ causing an _____ in circuit current. The voltage drops across each resistor will increase, except for the resistor that decreased in value. The voltage drop across the resistor that decreased will _____ by the same amount as the sum of the change in voltage drops across all the other resistors.

Series Circuits: Level III

Name_____ Class_____ Date _____

Objectives   Upon completion of this experiment, you should be able to:

- Observe the characteristics of a series circuit, using a common reference point.

- Understand how voltage polarity is determined, when using a common reference point, in a series circuit.

- Observe how a common reference point allows voltage comparisons in a series circuit.

- Understand how a common reference point is used to draw series circuits.

Text Reference   Terrell, *Fundamentals of Electronics: DC/AC Circuits*
        Chapter 4, Sections 4-1 through 4-5

Materials Required   Voltmeter
Variable power supply; 0 to 20 volts dc
1-kΩ resistor
3.3-kΩ resistor
Various test leads

Introduction

In the previous series circuits lab experiments, the voltage drops across resistors were measured with no regard to how the meter leads were placed across the component. Placing the leads one way across the resistor causes a negative voltage, reversing the leads will cause a positive voltage measurement. This makes it difficult to make voltage comparisons. Which direction is current flowing? What polarity of voltage is being measured in comparison to other resistor voltages? How large is the voltage at one point in comparison to the voltage at another point? All of these questions can be answered if a common point of reference is used to measure all voltages.

Observe Figure 12-1; notice that Point C has been chosen as the reference point. We know this because the reference symbol for a common point has been drawn at Point C. This symbol is commonly used in electronics for the common reference point and will be used as such throughout this lab manual.

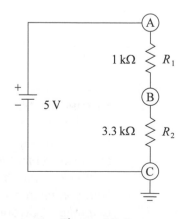

Figure 12-1

A common reference point allows voltage measurements to be taken with one point of reference. With a common point of reference, polarity of voltage measurements can be established. In most electronic circuits the common reference point can be chassis ground or it can be earth ground, depending on the system. Either the negative or the positive side of a dc power supply can also establish a common reference point. The common reference point in Figure 12-1 is the negative side of the power supply. The common lead (black lead) of the voltmeter, or negative lead in some cases, will always be attached to this point. Attaching the common lead of the voltmeter to this point, and using the red lead to measure different voltages answers the questions asked earlier in the Introduction.

The objective to is answer the questions, using the common reference point.

Procedures

1. Construct the circuit shown in Figure 12-1.

    Discussion The common reference point at Point C will be established when the voltmeter common lead is connected at that point. In a schematic diagram the common reference point is designated by the symbol at Point C. This indicates where the common lead, normally the black lead, is to be connected. Some schematics diagrams will include voltage levels at indicated points. In order to verify the indicated voltage levels, the voltmeter must connect to the same reference point.

2. **Turn on the power supply** and measure the voltage drop across R_1 and R_2 in Figure 12-1, without regard to polarity. Record each value in Table 12-1.

RESISTOR	VOLTAGES
V_{R_1}	
V_{R_2}	

Table 12-1

3. Measure the voltage at each point in the circuit and record the voltages measured in Table 12-2.

    Discussion Make sure that the common ground lead of the voltmeter is placed at Point C and **does not move** when measuring the different points in the circuit.

    Note that there is only one point (subscript) indicated in Table 12-2, (V_A), therefore the measurement is made from the point named (red lead at P oint A) to the common reference point, (black lead at P oint C). If the measurement were not to be made to the common reference point, both points (subscripts) of measurement would be indicated. Example: V_{AB} would indicate that Point A was being measured (red lead) with respect to Point B (black lead).

POINT	VOLTAGES
V_A	
V_B	
V_C	

Table 12-2

4. State in your own words why V_C is zero volts.

Discussion   Because the common lead and the red lead are at Point C, there is no difference of potential; hence, zero volts.

---

5. Move the common lead (black lead) of the voltmeter to Point B. Redraw the circuit, moving the ground symbol that is at Point C to Point B. Use the redrawn circuit for Table 12-3 measurements.

   Note   Remember **not to move the common lead** of the voltmeter until instructed.

6. At what point is the new common reference point?

7. Measure the voltage at each of the points indicated by Table 12-3 and record your readings.

POINT VOLTAGE VALUES	
Point A	
Point B	
Point C	

Table 12-3

8. What differences did you observe in comparing the readings in Table 12-1, Table 12-2, and Table 12-3?

Discussion   Note that V_A, in Table 12-3, is equal in value to the voltage measured across R_1 in Table 12-1. However, in Table 12-3, the voltage was positive. The voltage measured in Table 12-1 could have been a negative or a positive value. Voltage is negative or positive only in reference to a common reference point.

The voltage at Point C was negative with respect to the common reference point in Table 12-3 or when Point B was the common reference point. Remember that in Table 12-1 the measured voltage was zero volts. Point B measured zero volts in Table 12-3; therefore, the common reference point will be the zero-volt point of the circuit.

Draw the current through each component of Figure 12-1, indicating the polarity of voltage across each resistor. Starting at the negative side of the voltage source, go through R_2, negative on the bottom and positive on the top. Through R_1, negative at the bottom of the resistor and positive at the top. Then complete the path to the positive side of the voltage source.

Note that Point C is closer to the end of the resistor that is marked negative. This makes the voltage negative when the common reference point is Point B.

The voltages measured in Table 12-2 are positive. Observe the polarity markings for each resistor and observe that the positive side of the resistor is where the red lead was placed when the points indicated were measured. The voltage at Point A is the sum of the voltages across R_1 and R_2. At Point B the voltage is equal to the voltage across R_2, again positive.

9. Now move the common lead of the voltmeter (black lead) to Point A by redrawing the circuit and placing the ground symbol at Point A. Use the redrawn circuit as a reference for Table 12-4. Measure the voltages at each point in the circuit as indicated by Table 12-4.

POINT VOLTAGE VALUES	
Point A	
Point B	
Point C	

Table 12-4

10. Compare the values in Table 12-2 to the values in Tables 12-3 and 12-4 and answer the following questions:

   a. Is the absolute value of V_A (Table 12-2) equal to the absolute value of V_C?

   b. Do these measurements, V_A of Table 12-2 and V_C of Table 12-4, have the same polarity?

   c. What caused the change in polarity?

    d. Describe the differences between the voltage values listed for V_A in Tables 12-3 and 12-4.

Discussion   Even though the absolute values listed in Tables 12-2 and 12-4 are the same, the polarity changed because a change in the common reference point occurred. A change in the reference point does **not** change the value of the voltage, only its polarity.

   In Table 12-3, V_A is across R_1 and Point B is the reference point. In Table 12-4, both meter leads are at the same point in the circuit and no difference of potential exists.

Observations

Using what was observed, answer the following questions, compare answers with other lab teams, and discuss differences noted in the answers.

1. How many common reference points should one circuit have at any given time?

2. The voltage measured at a common reference point will be _____ volts. (Observe Table 12-2 when V_C was measured, Table 12-3 when V_B was measured, and Table 12-4 when V_A was measured.)

3. Does changing the common reference point change the value of voltage across a resistor?

4. Does the polarity of the voltage **always** change when a change in common reference points occurs?

5. Is the negative side of the power source always the common reference point?

Discussion   Because a given point is **common**, it is normal to redraw Figure 12-1 as shown in Figure 12-2. Even though Point C does not appear to be connected to the negative side of the power supply, it is connected because the same symbol appears at Point C and on the negative side of the power supply. In most cases it is easier to draw circuits in this fashion.

The common reference point is the zero-volt point of **every** circuit.

It is very common to draw circuits as shown in Figure 12-2. Remember, the common reference symbol is used to signify a **common point** This symbol indicates that points are connected or are the same point in the circuit. Again, the common reference point is always the zero-volt reference point of **every** circuit.

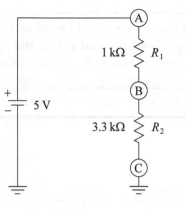

Figure 12-2

Series Circuits: Level IV

Name_____ Class_____ Date _____

Objectives Upon completion of this experiment, you should be able to:

- Further observe the characteristics of a series circuit, using a common reference point.

- Use a single reference point for voltage comparisons and voltage value determinations.

- Use a common reference point to troubleshoot series circuits.

Text Reference Terrell, *Fundamentals of Electronics: DC/AC Circuits*
Chapter 4, Sections 4-1 through 4-5

Materials Required Voltmeter
Variable power supply; 0 to 20 volts dc
1-kΩ resistor
2.2-kΩ resistor
2.7-kΩ resistor
3.3-kΩ resistor
6.8-kΩ resistor
Various test leads

Introduction

In most "real world" circuits, it is not possible to move the common reference point. They are, in effect, fixed. Sometimes it is necessary to leave the common lead in one place and measure voltages at different points. In those situations use simple addition and subtraction to determine individual component voltages values.

This experiment will use procedural steps to determine individual component values when one reference point is available. This will be an important aid in future troubleshooting projects.

Procedures

1. Construct the circuit shown in Figure 13-1.

Discussion The common reference point is at Point F; therefore, the voltmeter common lead is connected to this point. When given a schematic diagram, the common reference point is designated by the symbol indicated at Point F. This determines where the common lead, normally the black lead, is to be connected. Some schematic diagrams will include

voltage levels at indicated points. In order to verify the indicated voltage levels, the
voltmeter must be connected to the same common reference point.

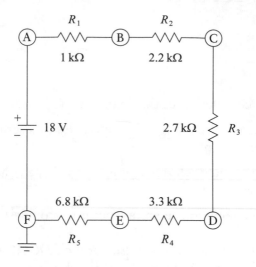

Figure 13-1

2. Measure the voltage drop for each resistor in Figure 13-1, without regard to polarity.
Record each value in Table 13-1.

RESISTOR	VOLTAGE VALUES
V_{R_1}	
V_{R_2}	
V_{R_3}	
V_{R_4}	
V_{R_5}	

Table 13-1

3. Measure the voltage at each point in the circuit and record the voltages measured in
Table 13-2.

Discussion   Make sure that the common lead of the voltmeter is placed at Point F and
does not move. Remember that there is only one point indicated in Table 13-2 (V_A).
Therefore, the measurement is made from the point named (red lead) to the common
reference point (black lead).

POINTS	VOLTAGE VALUES
V_A	
V_B	
V_C	
V_D	
V_E	

Table 13-2

---

4. State in your own words why Point F was not measured.

   How much voltage would be measured at Point F with respect to the common reference point?

Discussion   The voltage at any reference point should be zero volts.

   The voltage at Point A, in reference to Point F, measures the applied voltage or the sum of the voltages across each resistor. The voltage at Point B measures the sum of the voltages across R_2, R_3, R_4, and R_5. Therefore, if the voltage at Point B is subtracted from the voltage at Point A, the voltage across R_1 can be determined. This type of procedure can be used to determine the voltage across any component is a series circuit.

---

5. Determine the voltage drop across R_4 by subtracting the voltage at Point E from the voltage at Point D.

$$V_D - V_E = V_{R_4}$$

   {_____ volts} – {_____ volts} = _____ volts

6. Does this voltage compare to the value of voltage recorded in Table 13-1 for V_{R_4}? Use the absolute values to make comparisons.

Discussion   Remember that voltage is the difference of potential between two points. Therefore, if the voltages at Point D and at Point E are known, then V_{R_4} is the **difference** between these two voltages.

7. Show how to determine the voltage across the following resistors using the procedure in Step 5. Indicate the points to be used and the voltage levels to be subtracted.

a. V_{R_2} = {_____} – {_____}

b. V_{R_3} = {_____} – {_____}

c. V_{R_1} = {_____} – {_____}

How do these determined values compare to the values indicated in Table 13-1?

Discussion   This procedure can be used in any series circuit to measure individual component voltage drops. It is a very powerful troubleshooting tool when used properly. The following set of procedures give an example of how to use this technique.

8. **Turn off the power supply** and remove R_3 from the circuit.

Discussion   When a component is removed from the circuit, a gap should be left and no connection made to bridge the break in the circuit.

9. Turn on the power supply and measure V_D.

V_D = _____ volts

10. Measure V_C.

V_C = _____ volts

State, in your own words, your observations about the two voltage measurements. Your statement should include comments concerning the current in the circuit when measuring V_D and V_C.

Discussion   The voltage at Point D should have been zero volts, whereas the voltage at Point C should have been very close to the applied voltage of 18 volts.

When the meter was placed at Point D there was not a complete path for current through the voltmeter back to the power supply, therefore zero volts. When the voltmeter was placed at Point C there was a complete path for current through the meter to the power supply. Think of the voltmeter as a very large resistor. If using a DMM, this resistance is probably around ten megaohms. When the voltmeter is placed at Point C (refer to

Figure 13-2), it provides a complete path for current: through the voltmeter, through R_1 and R_2, and then back to the positive side of the applied voltage. Remember that the voltmeter resistance is very large and in a series circuit the largest resistor has the largest voltage drop. The voltmeter resistance is at least 10 times larger than the sum of R_1 and R_2. Therefore, the voltage drop across the meter is much larger than the voltage across R_1 and R_2.

If the applied voltage is measured at V_C, then an open circuit exists between the common reference point and Point C. Remember that the voltage at Point D was zero volts, which indicates no complete path for current; however, the voltage at Point C was equal to the applied voltage. The only component between Point C and D is R_3.

Because R_3 is the only resistor between these two points, it must be open.

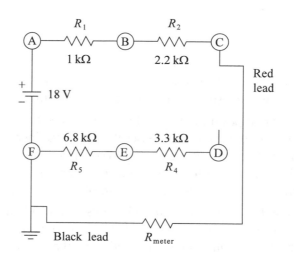

Figure 13-2

---

11. Remove the meter and **turn off the power supply.**

12. Take a piece of wire and place it between Points C and D.

13. Turn on the power supply and measure the voltage at Point C and at Point D.

    $V_C =$ _____ volts

    $V_D =$ _____ volts

    State your observations about the voltages measured at these two points.

14. **Turn off the power supply. Place R_3 in its normal position, without removing the jumper wire.**

15. Measure the voltage at Point C and at Point D.

    $V_C =$ _____ volts

    $V_D =$ _____ volts

    State your observations about these measurements using the values obtained in Steps 13 and 15 as a reference.

Discussion   Normally resistors do not short. When the term "short" is used, it refers to zero ohms or so close to zero ohms as to be not measurable.

   Carbon composition or thin film resistors have a positive temperature coefficient; as the temperature of the resistor increases the resistance increases. When a resistor exceeds its power rating (in watts), it usually opens or has infinite resistance. There are rare occasions when wire-wound resistors will short. However, other components will short. This gives us an opportunity to observe the effect of zero ohms in a circuit.

   Each of the voltages measured in Steps 13 and 15 should have been the same value. This indicates no difference of potential between two points in a circuit. According to Ohm's Law, if there is no difference of potential or voltage, then the resistance must also be equal to zero ohms.

---

16. Without removing the jumper wire, thereby shorting out R_3, state other characteristics of the series circuit that changed when the jumper was installed. State whether values increased or decreased. (Be sure to include total circuit resistance, total circuit current, and individual resistor voltage drops: V_{R_1}, V_{R_2}, and so on.)

17. With the jumper still installed, measure the following values to prove the answers listed in Step 16.

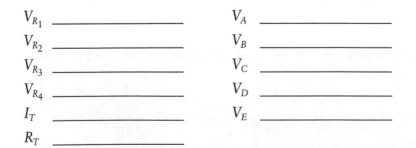

V_{R_1} _____ V_A _____

V_{R_2} _____ V_B _____

V_{R_3} _____ V_C _____

V_{R_4} _____ V_D _____

I_T _____ V_E _____

R_T _____

Note   Remember to turn off the power supply and remove the power supply leads before measuring total resistance of the circuit (between Points A and F) with an ohmmeter.

Observations

1. State what observations were made regarding "opens" or high resistance values in comparison to "shorts" or low resistance values.

2. State what observations were made regarding measuring and determining voltage drops across components when using one common reference point.

Series Circuits: Level V

Name _____ Class _____ Date _____

Objectives   Upon completion of this experiment, you should be able to:

- Create a series circuit that has the stated voltages at given points.

Text Reference   Terrell, *Fundamentals of Electronics: DC/AC Circuits*
Chapter 4, Sections 4-1 through 4-5

Materials Required   Voltmeter
Ohmmeter
Current meter
Variable power supply; 0 to 20 volts dc
Various resistors
Various test leads

Introduction

By way of introduction to the highest level experiments for each group, these projects are intended for those who finish the lower levels. There will be a few or no procedures to follow. The project will state a problem or problems to be solved. The solution to the problem is to construct a circuit that will satisfy the problem requirements. The applied voltage and required voltage levels may or may not be given and a maximum current level may be specified, but no resistor values will be given.

Your or your team's solution may have different values from other teams or individuals. As long as your circuit meets the parameters of the problem it is correct.

You may want to review all of the series circuit experiments to find possible hints to the solution. All of the information gained from previous experiments may be a part of the solution. Use what you have learned to discover different ways of using the information to learn new ways of solving series circuits problems. The text can also be a resource.

When completing this project make sure you save all calculations and work involved in the solution to the problem(s).

Procedures

PROBLEM 1

1. Using Figure 14-1 as a guide, calculate the resistor values necessary to have the voltages at the indicated points.

The total circuit current should not exceed 20 mA.

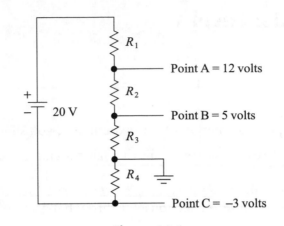

Figure 14-1

$R_1 =$ _____ Ω

$R_2 =$ _____ Ω

$R_3 =$ _____ Ω

$R_4 =$ _____ Ω

Discussion   If a calculated resistor value is not a standard value, select the next larger value or use a variable resistor.

2. Determine the power being dissipated by each resistor in the given circuited.

$P_{R_1} =$ _____

$P_{R_2} =$ _____

$P_{R_3} =$ _____

$P_{R_4} =$ _____

Discussion   Make sure each resistor will not exceed the power rating of the resistors. If the power rating of just one resistor is exceeded, the value of total circuit current will need to be decreased.

3. Construct the circuit in Figure 14-1, using the calculated values.

4. Have the circuit verified for proper operation, showing all work used to determine circuit resistor values.

PROBLEM 2

5. Draw and construct a series circuit where the voltage from one point in the circuit, in respect to a common reference point, will vary from 1 volt to the applied voltage minus 1 volt.

Example   Applied voltage equals 20 volts. The voltage at one point in the circuit equals 1 volt to 19 volts.

The minimum number of resistors that may be used is three (3). However, any type of resistor may be used as long as there is an adjustment for the voltage and it varies as stated above. (*Hint:* variable resistor)

Make sure that each resistor's power rating is not exceeded.

Observations

1. Show how to determine the resistance value for a given voltage value in the circuit you constructed for Problem 2.

Resistive Parallel Circuits: Level I

Name __Donivan McGirel__   Class __DC Electronics__ Date __07/21/04__

Objectives   Upon completion of this experiment, you should be able to:

- Observe that the total current is the sum of the individual branch currents.

- Observe that the total resistance is less than the smallest resistor.

- Observe that the voltage across each branch is equal to the applied voltage.

- Determine the individual branch currents by using a current meter.

Text Reference   Terrell, *Fundamentals of Electronics: DC/AC Circuits*
        Chapter 5, Sections 5-1 through 5-4

Materials Required   DMM or VOM
Variable power supply; 2 to 20 volts dc
1-kΩ resistor
2.2-kΩ resistor
3.3-kΩ resistor
Jumper wires (4)
Various test leads

Introduction

In this experiment jumper wire will be used to cause gaps or "opens" in the circuit or to make a circuit connection. A jumper wire is a piece of wire that is used to connect one part of a circuit to another. For this experiment four jumper wires will be required. Make the jumper wires long enough to reach any part of the circuit, stripping each end of the wire.

Observe Figure 15-1 in the Procedures section and note the curved lines that appear below each resistor (A to A', B to B', and C to C') and the curved line connected to the positive side of the power supply (D to D'). These curved lines represent jumper wires. These wires provide an easy method to break the circuit when using the current meter. The current meter will replace the jumper wire when measuring individual branch currents (A through C) or total current (D). Referring to the different points, such as A or A', will help you to connect the meter properly and with correct polarity.

Procedures

1. Using an ohmmeter, measure the resistors listed in Table 15-1.

RESISTOR VALUES	
1 kΩ	975 Ω
2.2 kΩ	~~2108~~ Ω 2,117
3.3 kΩ	3,280 Ω

Table 15-1

2. Construct the circuit shown in Figure 15-1, placing the jumper wires for easy access.

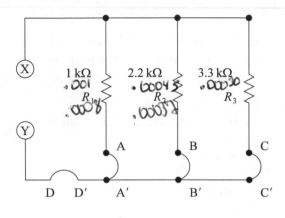

Figure 15-1

3. Place the ohmmeter between Points X and Y and record the total resistance indicated by the ohmmeter.

    __560__ Ω

4. Is the total resistance smaller than the smallest resistor?

    Yes

    Note   Remember the looped lines represent jumper wires in the circuit.

5. With the ohmmeter still connected to Points X and Y, remove the jumper wire connected between **Points A and A'** and state your observations about the ohmmeter indication.

Discussion The total measured resistance (Step 3) should be around 560 Ω, which is smaller than the smallest resistor. The observation in Step 5 should state that the resistance increased when the jumper wire was removed. The indication in Step 5 should be about 1320 Ω. Further investigation will determine why this occurs.

6. Reconnect the jumper wire to Point A.

7. Turn the voltage control of the power supply to minimum. Connect the power supply to Points X and Y—the negative lead to Point Y and the positive lead to Point X. Adjust the power supply for 10 volts.

8. Measure the voltage across each resistor and state your observations.

   Voltage across each resistor is the same as applied voltage ie 10 volts

Discussion The observations should state that all of the voltages measured were the same value. The voltages measured should also equal the applied voltage.

9. **Turn off the power supply.** Disconnect the jumper wire between **Points D and D′.**

   If the current meter were inserted into the gap left by the missing jumper wire, which current would be measured?

   ☑ I_{R_1}

   ☐ I_{R_2}

   ☐ I_{R_3}

   ☐ I_T

10. Insert the current meter into the gap left by the removal of the jumper wire that was between Points D and D′.

    Make sure that the current range is higher than 20 mA and that polarity is observed.

    Turn on the power supply and record the total circuit current in Table 15-2.

11. **Turn off the power supply. Remove the current meter and reconnect the Point D jumper wire.**

12. Calculate the value of current through R1, using the measured value of R_1 from Table 15-1.

$$\frac{V_{R_1}}{R_1} = I_{R_1} \quad 10\,mA$$

13. Disconnect the jumper wire from **Point A and A′**, leaving the jumper wire connected to Point A′. Connect the common lead of the current meter to the wire and the red lead of the current meter to the resistor that the wire was connected to.

    Trace current through R_1 to make sure the current meter is in **series** with the 1-kΩ resistor. Make sure that the current range for the meter is higher than the calculated value and that the polarity is observed.

14. Turn on the power supply and record the indicated current value through R_1 in Table 15-2.

CURRENT VALUES	
I_{R_1}	10.2 mA
I_{R_2}	4.7 mA
I_{R_3}	3 mA
I_{Total}	18 mA

Table 15-2

15. **Turn off the power supply,** remove the current meter, and reconnect the Point A jumper wire.

16. Repeat Steps 12 through 15 for Points B and B′ and Points C and C′ jumper wires, recording the indicated values in Table 15-2 for the current measured through R_2 and R_3.

    Calculated value of I_{R_2} = ___4.5 mA___ mA.

    Calculated value of I_{R_3} = ___3.04___ mA.

17. Add the calculated currents together.

$$I_{R_1} + I_{R_2} + I_{R_3} = I_{Total}$$

    Calculated total current ___17.54___ mA.

18. Add the measured currents together.
    Measured total current ___18 mA___ mA.

Discussion   The calculated total circuit current and the measured total circuit current values should be relatively close. What has been observed is that the sum of the branch currents is the total circuit current. The total circuit current should be approximately 17.5 mA.

---

19. Using the value for the total resistance measured in Step 3, determine the total circuit current.

$$\frac{V_{Applied}}{R_{T\ Measured}} = I_{Total}$$

I_{Total} = ___17.85___ mA

20. How does this value (Step 19) compare to the previous values estimated and measured (Steps 17 and 18)?

Value is off by .5 mA due to different Ω readings for selected resistors

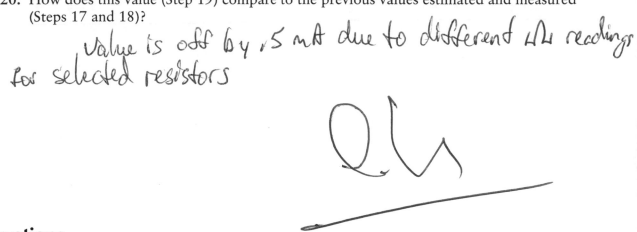

Observations

1. If R_1, in Figure 15-1, is replaced with a 1200-Ω resistor, will the total resistance increase or decrease?

   The total resistance will increase

2. If R_2, in Figure 15-1, is replaced with a 2.7-kΩ resistor, will there be a large increase in total resistance (greater than 500 Ω)? *No total resistance only increased by 40 Ω*

3. If the applied voltage is increased to 15 volts, state what will happen to the following values:

	Increase ↑	Decrease ↓	Remain the same ↔
V_{R_1}			*15 volts*
R_{Total}			*560 Ω*
I_{R_2}	*6.8 mA*		
I_{Total}	*20 mA*		

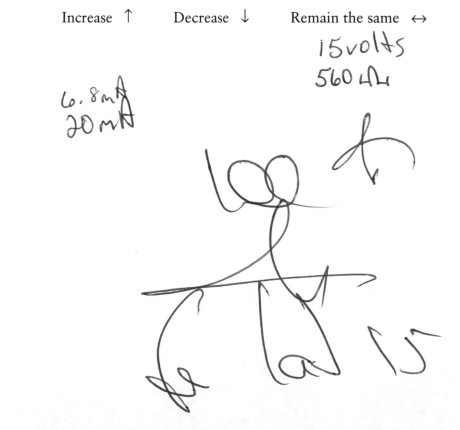

Experiment 16

Resistive Parallel Circuits: Level II

Name_____ Class_____ Date _____

Objectives   Upon completion of this experiment, you should be able to:

- Observe the effect on total circuit current and/or total circuit resistance when the applied voltage is varied.

- Observe the effect on total circuit current and/or total circuit resistance when the branch resistance is varied.

- Observe the effect on total circuit current and/or total circuit resistance as one branch resistance opens.

Text Reference   Terrell, *Fundamentals of Electronics: DC/AC Circuits*
      Chapter 5, Sections 5-1 through 5-4

Materials Required   Current meter
Voltmeter
Variable power supply; 0 to 20 volts dc
1-kΩ resistor
2.2-kΩ resistor
8.2-kΩ resistor
20–22 ga. jumper wires (2)
Various test leads

Introduction

Making observations is an important part of troubleshooting. The observations can be used to draw conclusions and the conclusions can be used to make an educated guess as to what changed in the circuit.

Changes in current and voltage are generally a result of a change in resistance. The observations will indicate whether the voltage across any component or the current through any component changed. Voltage drops are measured and from this information we can surmise if the resistance increased or decreased in value.

During this experiment keep a list observations. When you have completed this experiment, compare your observations with others. They may have made some that you did not and you may have observed some things that they did not. After you have listed your observations and compared them, write down two or three conclusions. Then compare them to the stated Objectives to see if you have learned what you need to know.

Procedures

1. Construct the circuit shown in Figure 16-1.

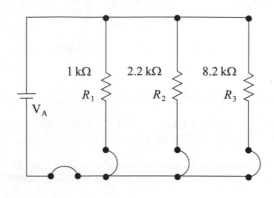

Figure 16-1

> **Note** Remember, the looped lines represent jumper wires in the circuit in Figure 16-1.

2. Set the current meter range to measure a current greater than 20 mA.

3. Connect the voltmeter to measure the power supply voltage. The voltage range on the voltmeter should be able to measure 20 volts.

4. **Slowly** adjust the power supply until I_{Total} is 20 mA, observing the voltage versus current relationship.

   What happened to the I_{Total} as the power supply voltage was increased?

5. **Turn off the power supply.** Do not adjust the voltage control setting.

6. Disconnect the current meter and install a jumper wire in place of the current meter. Remove the jumper in series with R_2 and insert the meter to measure I_{R2}.

7. Turn on the power supply and record the indicated current.

   $I_{R_2} = $ _____ mA.

8. **Turn off the power supply.** Do not adjust the voltage setting.

9. Disconnect the current meter and install a jumper wire in place of the current meter.

   Remove the jumper in series with R_3 and insert the meter to measure I_{R_3}.

10. Turn on the power supply and record the indicated current.

    $I_{R_3} = $ _____ mA.

11. Determine the current through R_1.

$$I_T - I_{R_2} - I_{R_3} = I_{R_1}$$

Discussion   Remember that the sum of the branch currents is equal to the total circuit current. By using the equation stated above, we can determine the current through R_1 by adding the branch current values and subtracting them from the total circuit current.

12. **Turn off the power supply.**

    Remove the current meter and reinstall the jumper wire.

13. Remove the jumper wire that will allow the current meter to measure the total circuit current and install the current meter.

14. Remove R_1 and replace it with a 6.8-kΩ resistor.

    ▼**CAUTION**   **Do not adjust the power supply control setting.**

15. Turn on the power supply and state what was observed about the total circuit current. Remember, the applied voltage was preset and did not change the total circuit current.

    What changed to cause a decrease in total circuit current?

16. **Turn off the power supply.**

    Remove the current meter and replace it with a jumper wire. Resistor R_1 is still a 6.8-kΩ resistor.

    Remove the jumper wire that creates a gap in series with R_1.

    Place the current meter in the gap.

    Turn on the power supply and measure I_{R1}.

    I_{R_1} = _____ mA.

17. Using the same procedures listed in Step 16, measure and record the indicated current through R_2 and R_3.

    I_{R_2} = _____ mA.

    I_{R_3} = _____ mA.

18. Did I_{R_2} and I_{R_3} change?

    Did I_{R_1} change?

What caused the change in I_{R_1}?

Did the total circuit resistance change?

Did the total circuit current change?

Discussion   In the original configuration of the circuit, resistor R_1 was the smallest resistor in the parallel circuit. When it was changed, R_2 became the smallest resistor. The smallest resistor will have the largest current through it. Even though the current through R_2 and R_3 did not change, the total circuit current became smaller, indicating an increase in total circuit resistance. No change in current occurred because the voltage across the resistors and the value of the resistors remained the same.

---

19. **Turn off the power supply.**

    Remove R_1.

20. Place the current meter in the circuit to measure the total circuit current.

    Turn on the power supply and measure the total circuit current.

    Did the total circuit current change?

21. Using previous procedures, measure the current through R_2 and R_3.

    $I_{R_2} =$ _____

    $I_{R_3} =$ _____

    Did I_{R_2} or I_{R_3} change?

Discussion   When R_1 was removed, one less current path existed. Therefore, current decreased, which indicates that an increase in resistance occurred. However, the individual resistor currents, I_{R_2} and I_{R_3} remained the same.

Observations

1. Did the voltage across any of the resistors ever change after the I_T was set to 20 mA.?

2. Whenever one of the branch resistances increases, a/an _____ in total circuit current will result.

3. When R_1 was removed from the circuit, which resistor had a larger current?

    ☐ R_1

    ☐ R_3

4. Use Figure 16-1 as a reference. Suppose the total circuit current decreased by a very small amount, which resistor would have opened?

    State the reason(s) for selecting this resistor.

Resistive Parallel Circuits: Level III

Name_____ Class_____ Date _____

Objectives   Upon completion of this experiment, you should be able to:

- Demonstrate the effect of a change in one branch's resistance on total circuit current and total resistance.

- Observe the effect of shorting and opening one branch's resistance on voltage measurements within the branch and total circuit current.

Text Reference   Terrell, *Fundamentals of Electronics: DC/AC Circuits*
    Chapter 5, Sections 5-1 through 5-4

Materials Required   Voltmeter
Current meter
Ohmmeter
Variable power supply; 0 to 20 volts dc
1-kΩ resistor
2.2-kΩ resistor
3.3-kΩ resistor
5-kΩ variable resistor
Three 22–20 gage jumper wires
Various test leads

Introduction

Sometimes more that one resistor makes up the total branch resistance. This experiment will introduce concepts that will be learned when series-parallel circuits are presented. In this experiment we want to observe how the parallel circuit is affected by changes within the branches of the parallel circuit. What effect will changing the resistance within a branch have on the circuit current and total resistance? These changes will determine the amount of power (in watts) the voltage source must supply. In a parallel circuit, if one branch shorts or the resistance is close to zero ohms, the voltage source could be damaged; a fuse in the voltage source could be blown; or circuit wiring could be damaged. Good troubleshooting techniques include how to detect this type of problem and fix the cause of the voltage source damage as well as the voltage source itself.

Notice in Figure 17-1 (see Procedures) that there are two resistors in one branch of the parallel circuit. The two resistors in one branch will be in series with each other.

When two components are connected end-to-end, with no other component connected at their junction, they are in series. If the same current flows through both components they are in series.

When two components or branches have both ends of both components connected together they are in parallel. If both ends of both branches are connected together they are also in parallel.

Observe Figure 17-1. Notice that the bottom of R_2 is connected to the bottom of R_3 and that the top of R_1 is connected to the top of R_3. These two branches are in parallel. However, the bottom of R_1 is connected to the top of R_2 with no other connection at their junction. The same current flows through both resistors. Therefore, R_1 and R_2 are in series. This series combination of R_1 and R_2 is in parallel with R_3. Notice also that R_3 is a rheostat and will be used to change the branch resistance.

The applied voltage of five (5) volts is the sum of the voltage drops across R_1 and R_2, while the voltage drop across R_3 is equal to the sum of the voltage drops across R_1 and R_2. The voltage across R_3 is equal to the source voltage; therefore, the sum of the voltage drops across R_1 and R_2 is also equal to the source voltage.

Procedures

1. Construct the circuit shown in Figure 17-1, inserting the three jumper wires as shown. Adjust R_2 for 3-kΩ.

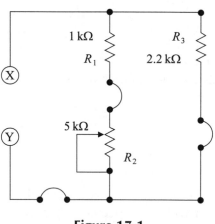

Figure 17-1

2. Using the ohmmeter, measure the total circuit resistance between Points X and Y.

    _____ Ω

3. With the ohmmeter still connected, remove R_1 from the circuit and state your observations about the change in the total circuit resistance.

What value does this measurement approximate?

4. Place a jumper wire in the gap left by the removal of R_1 and state your observations about the change in the total circuit resistance.

5. Remove the jumper wire and reinstall R_1.

6. Slowly adjust R_2 CCW and observe the ohmmeter indications while adjusting. State your observations.

7. Slowly adjust R_2 CW and observe the ohmmeter indications while adjusting. State your observations.

8. Remove R_2, the variable resistor, and replace it with a 3.3-kΩ resistor.

   Record the ohmmeter indication between Points X and Y with the 3.3-kΩ resistor installed.

   _____ Ω

9. Observe Figure 17-2 and calculate the value of the total circuit current, using the total resistance value measured in Step 8.

   $I_T =$ _____ mA

10. Connect the power supply and adjust it for 5 volts dc as shown in Figure 17-2.

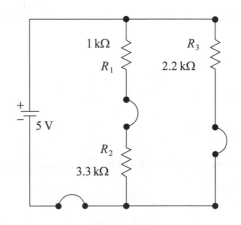

Figure 17-2

11. **Turn off the power supply,** remove the jumper that will allow the total circuit current to be measured, and connect the current meter. The current range of the meter should be set to measure a value of current greater than 5 mA.

12. Turn on the power supply and record the indicated current.

    _____ mA

13. **Turn off the power supply.**

    Remove the current meter and reinstall the jumper wire.

    Remove the jumper between R_1 and R_2 and connect the current meter into the branch circuit.

14. Determine the value of current that flows through R_1 and R_2.

    _____ mA

    Turn on the power supply and record the measured branch current value.

    _____ mA

    Based on the measurement of R_1 and R_2 branch current, how much current flows through resistor R_3?

    $I_{R_3} =$ _____ mA

    State what procedures would be used to measure the current through R_3.

15. **Turn off the power supply.**

    Remove R_1 from the circuit. When removing R_1, make sure the positive or red lead of the current meter is not connected.

16. Turn on the power supply and state your observations about the change in branch current.

    With R_1 removed, did the total circuit current decrease? Repeat Steps 10 and 11 to prove your answer.

17. With the current meter installed to measure the R_1 and R_2 branch current and R_1 removed, measure the voltage drop directly across R_2 and state your observations.

18. Without removing the current meter, measure the voltage across the gap left by the removal of R_1 and state your observations. When making this voltage measurement, connect the black lead of the voltmeter to the red lead of the current meter and the red lead of the voltmeter to the wire that connects to the positive side of the voltage source.

19. When the voltage across an open R_1 was being measured, what indications were on the branch circuit current meter? Use the smallest current range, if necessary, to measure any value of current.

Discussion   When the total circuit current was measured with R_1 open, the current indication was approximately equal to 5 volts divided by 3.3 kΩ. This indicates that the second branch with R_3 is working normally.

When the voltmeter replaced R_1, a complete path for current was created by the voltmeter. Trace the current from the negative side of the source, through R_2, through the voltmeter and back to the positive side of the voltage source. Although this current will be small, with the gap in the branch and no voltmeter, **no** current will flow though this branch.

The value of voltage across the gap left by the removal of R_1 should have been very close to the applied voltage. This indicates that the dc resistance of the meter is much higher than R_2 (2.2 kΩ). The dc resistance of the meter could be determined by dividing the voltage indication (Step 18) by the current indication (Step 19). If you are using a DMM, the answer should be around 10 megaohms. This accounts for the small current indication.

The important part of this observation should be that the voltmeter completes the path for current. When you measured R_2, zero volts should have been the indication. The conclusion is that there is no current through the meter and therefore no indication of voltage. Understanding this concept is very important in troubleshooting. When the voltage across the open was measured, a current did flow through the voltmeter; therefore, a voltage indication was observed.

---

20. **Turn off the power supply.**

    Place R_1 in the circuit.

21. Take the third jumper wire and place it across R_1 in parallel with the resistor.

    ⚡CAUTION **Make sure that the jumper wire is only across R_1, not R_1 and R_2. If it is across both resistors, the power supply may be damaged if the current limit is not properly set.**

    Discussion The current limit control adjusts the power supply's maximum current limit. If this limit is exceeded, the output voltage will drop to zero and generally an indicator light will turn on. This is a safety feature to prevent damage caused by excessive current draw from the power supply.

22. Turn on the power supply and record the branch circuit current.

    _____ mA

    Is this value larger or smaller than the value measured in Step 14? Explain why you think the value changed; include branch resistance in your explanation.

    With the voltmeter, measure the voltage across R_2 and state your observation.

    Measure the voltage across R_1 and state your observation.

Discussion   In this case the voltage across R_2 is equal to the applied voltage and the current indication is much higher than normal. The voltage across R_1 is zero volts, indicating that the resistance is zero ohms. We have current and no voltage across R_1; therefore, the resistance must be zero.

How did we know that R_2 was not open? If R_2 was open, the current through the voltmeter would have been a much lower value. The current indication would have been approximately 5 volts divided by 10 megaohms, instead of 5 volts divided by 2.2 kΩ.

Observations

1. State your observations about the voltage across an open.

2. State your observations about the current when a open exists.

3. State your observations about the voltage across a short or when zero ohms occurs.

4. State your observations about what the current value does as the resistance value approaches zero ohms.

5. If you are measuring circuit voltage and the voltmeter measures zero volts, is the voltmeter across the open in the circuit?

6. If you are measuring circuit voltage and the DMM measures the applied voltage across a branch of the parallel circuit, does the open exist between the meter leads or outside the meter leads?

Resistive Parallel Circuits: Level IV

Name _____ Class _____ Date _____

Objectives Upon completion of this experiment, you should be able to:

- Construct a parallel circuit that will meet the circuit criteria.

Text Reference Terrell, *Fundamentals of Electronics: DC/AC Circuits*
    Chapter 5, Sections 5-1 through 5-4

Materials Needed Current meter
    Voltmeter
    Variable power supply
    Various resistors
    Various test leads

Introduction

Using the information observed and learned in previous experiments, one can design a parallel circuit that will provide different currents. Review this information and use the text as an aid. Remember that variable resistors can be used as rheostats to change the branch current.

Procedures

1. Design and construct a circuit that will meet the following load requirements:

    a. One ten-volt power supply is connected to three parallel branches.

    b. Branch #1 must have a current of 5 mA.

    c. Branch #2 must have a current of 2.5 mA.

    d. Branch #3 must have a current of 6.6 mA.

    Place a jumper wire so that each branch current can be measured as well as the total circuit current.

    Simulate the loads by using resistors.

    Show all calculations required to meet the circuit criteria.

Draw the schematic diagram.

Observations

1. If the current in Branch #2 needs to be increased to 6 mA, then the resistive load would need to be _____ to _____ Ω.

2. If the current in Branch #3 needs to be decreased to 4.5 mA, then the branch resistance needs to be _____ to _____ Ω.

3. If the applied voltage is decreased to 8 volts and the branch resistors retain the same values, show by calculations what each branch current and the total circuit current will become.

Resistive Series Parallel Circuits: Level I

Name _Donivan McGreal_ Class _D.C. Electronics_ Date _07/28/06_

Objectives Upon completion of this experiment, you should be able to:

- Determine the relationship (series or parallel) between resistors in a resistive series-parallel circuit.

- Observe that the total circuit current is the sum of the branch currents.

- Recognize that the sum of the voltage drops around each complete path for current is equal to the applied voltage.

Text Reference Terrell, *Fundamentals of Electronics: DC/AC Circuits*
    Chapter 6, Sections 6-1 through 6-4

Materials Required Current meter
Ohmmeter
Voltmeter
Variable power supply; 0 to 20 volts dc
4.7-kΩ resistor
2.7-kΩ resistor
1.5-kΩ resistor
Various test leads

Introduction

Rule 1 If two resistors are connected end-to-end, with **no** other connection at their junction, they are in series.

Rule 2 If **both** ends of both resistors are connected, the resistors are in parallel.

Almost all series-parallel resistive circuits can be simplified by finding the total circuit resistance. This can be accomplished by using the above stated rules and taking small steps.

With each new circuit, trace all current paths. This will aid in determining the relationship of the resistors, show which resistors have total circuit current, and establish complete current loops. The sum of the voltages around these complete current loops must equal the applied voltage. In some series-parallel circuits there may be more than one complete path for current.

Redrawing the circuits as the resistors are combined is always a good practice.

Procedures

1. Measure the actual value of each resistor and record this value in Table 19-1.

RESISTOR VALUES	
1.5 kΩ	1.43 Kɯɲ
2.7 kΩ	2.6 Kɯɾ
4.7 kΩ	4.5 Rɯɲ

Table 19-1

2. Connect the circuit as shown in Figure 19-1.

3. State the relationship between R_2 and R_3. Is it series or parallel?
   Parallel

4. Using the actual resistor values listed in Table 19-1, determine the equivalent resistance of R_2 and R_3 in parallel.
   R_{eq} = 1.7 Kɯɲ

Discussion   The equivalent resistance should have been:

$$R_{eq} = \frac{R_2 \times R_3}{R_2 + R_3} = \frac{2.7\ k \times 4.7\ k}{2.7\ k + 4.7\ k} = 1.72\ k\Omega$$

Now redraw the circuit using the equivalent resistance and R_1.

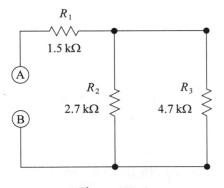

Figure 19-1

5. State the relationship between the equivalent resistance and R_1. Is it series or parallel?
   Series

6. Using the actual value of R_1 listed in Table 19-1 and the equivalent resistance determined in Step 4, determine the total circuit resistance.
   Calculated value of R_{Total} = 3.22 K Ω

Discussion The total circuit resistance should have been:

$$R_{eq} + R_1 = 1.72 \text{ k}\Omega + 1.5 \text{ k}\Omega = 3.22 \text{ k}\Omega$$

---

7. Using the ohmmeter, measure the total resistance between Points A and B.
   Measured value of R_{Total} = ___3.12K___ Ω

8. Using Figure 19-2, trace all current paths.

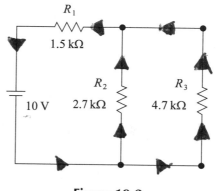

Figure 19-2

Determine the total circuit current, using the measured value of total resistance obtained in Step 7.

I_T = ___3.2___ mA

9. What is the value of current flowing through R_1?

I_{R_1} = ___3.14___ mA

Discussion The current through R_1 should have been 3.1 mA (the total circuit current). The total circuit current is the sum of all branch currents. Kirchhoff's Current Law states that the sum of the currents entering a point **must** be equal to the sum of the currents leaving that point.

---

10. Calculate the voltage across R_1.

V_{R_1} = ___4.8___ V

11. Calculate the voltage across R_2 and R_3.

$V_{R_2} = V_{R_3}$ = ___5.2___ V

12. Using the actual values listed in Table 19-1, calculate the current through resistors R_2 and R_3.

I_{R_2} = ___1.9___ mA

I_{R_3} = ___1.2___ mA

13. Determine the value of I_T by adding the two branch currents together.

    $I_T =$ ___3.10___ mA

    Is this the same current value as determined in Step 9?

    Yes

14. Does the sum of V_{R_1} and V_{R_2} equal the applied voltage?

    Yes

    Does the sum of V_{R_1} and V_{R_3} equal the applied voltage?

    Yes

15. Construct the circuit shown in Figure 19-2.

    It may be convenient to install jumper wires to allow insertion of the current meter to measure I_T or I_{R_1}, I_{R_2}, and I_{R_3}.

16. Measure each of the currents indicated in Table 19-2.

CURRENT VALUES	
I_{R_1} or I_T	3.18 mA
I_{R_2}	1.94 mA
I_{R_3}	1.24 mA

Table 19-2

17. Is the sum of I_{R_2} and I_{R_3} equal to I_{R_1} or I_T?

    Yes

18. Measure each of the voltage drops listed in Table 19-3.

VOLTAGE VALUES	
V_{Total}	10V
V_{R_1}	4.8V
V_{R_2}	5.2 V
V_{R_3}	5.2V

Table 19-3

19. What observations can be made about the sum of the voltage drops across R_1 and R_2, when compared to the current paths drawn in Figure 19-2? Can the same observations be made about the sum of the voltage drops across R_1 and R_3?

The Voltage drops across R_1 & R_2 equal the applied voltage. Voltage in a parallel circuit remains the same so voltage across R_2 & R_3 are the same. With this the Voltage drop across R_1 & R_3 equal the applied voltage

Observations

1. State what procedure steps were used to prove the following:

   The sum of the branch currents is equal to the total current.

   1) Finding the total resistance
   2) Taking applied voltage divided by total resistance
   3) Calculating the voltage drop across R_1 & R_2 & R_3
   4) Calculating current for R_1, R_2 & R_3

   The sum of the voltages around a complete path for current must be equal to the applied voltage.

   1) Once finding total resistance
   2) Finding current by total resistance divided into total voltage
   3) Once current achieved calculated the voltage drops across R_1, R_2 & R_3
   4) Double checking calculations equal to applied voltage

Resistive Series/Parallel Circuits: Level II

Name _____ Class _____ Date _____

Objectives   Upon completion of this experiment, you should be able to:

- Observe changes in total circuit current by monitoring changes in voltage drops across circuit resistances. The changes in current will occur because a resistance in the circuit changed.

- Observe how changes in circuit resistances affect branch currents and voltages.

Text   Terrell, *Fundamentals of Electronics: DC/AC Circuits*
Reference   Chapter 6, Sections 6-1 through 6-4

Materials   Voltmeter
Required   Ohmmeter
Variable power supply; 0 to 20 volts dc
4.7-kΩ resistor
2.7-kΩ resistor
1-kΩ resistor
10-kΩ variable resistor
5-kΩ variable resistor
Various test leads

Introduction

In real world circuits it is sometimes inconvenient to monitor circuit currents. Changes in circuit current can be detected by monitoring component voltages. In this experiment certain resistances will be varied and the variances that occur can be seen by observing the changes in component voltages.

The observed changes in voltage drops can generally be used to determine what component changed. When troubleshooting circuits, the changes in voltage will indicate the fault in the circuit.

Procedures

Refer to Figure 20-1 for the following steps.

1. Trace and label all current paths.

   (I_T, I_{R_3}, I_{R_4}, and I_{R_5})

2. If the 5-kΩ variable resistor is adjusted for 2.7 kΩ and the 10 kΩ variable resistor is adjusted for 3.7 kΩ, determine R_{Total}.

Discussion   Start at the far right hand side of the circuit, farthest away from the power supply. Establish the relationship between R_4 and R_5. Are they in series or parallel?

Because they are connected end-to-end with no other connection at their junction, they are in series. Therefore, add them together and redraw the circuit with one equivalent resistor for R_4 and R_5. What is the relation between R_3 and the equivalent resistance: series or parallel?

Because both ends of both R_3 and R_{eq} are connected together, they are in parallel. Find the equivalent resistance and redraw the circuit.

Now a series circuit exists with the equivalent resistance in series with R_1 and R_2. The sum of these values is the total resistance.

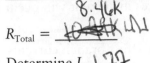

$R_{Total} = \underline{\quad 8.46k \quad \Omega \quad}$

3. Determine I_T. 1.77

   $I_T = \underline{\qquad mA}$

4. Determine each resistor voltage drop and list their values in the space provided on the schematic diagram in Figure 20-1.

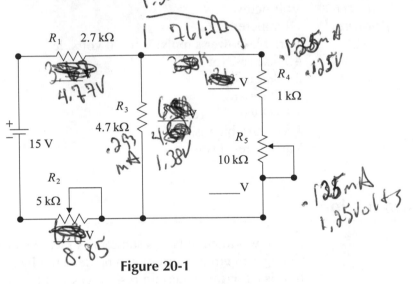

Figure 20-1

Discussion   Remember the total circuit current flows through R_1 and R_2, and the voltage across R_3 is the sum of the voltage drops across R_1 and R_2 subtracted from the applied voltage.

The sum of the voltage drops across R_4 and R_5 is equal to the voltage drop across R_3.

5. Show how to determine the current through R_3, R_4, and R_5. Start with I_{Total} and subtract each branch current.

6. Using the ohmmeter, adjust the 10-kΩ variable resistor for 3.7 kΩ.

   Adjust the 5-kΩ variable resistor for 2.7 kΩ.

7. Construct the circuit shown in Figure 20-1.

8. Turn on the power supply and adjust the voltage control for 15 volts.

9. Measure the voltage drops across each resistor. Verify the calculations made in Step 2, recording the measured voltages.

   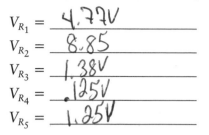

   $V_{R_1} =$ 4.79V

   $V_{R_2} =$ 8.85

   $V_{R_3} =$ 1.38V

   $V_{R_4} =$ .125V

   $V_{R_5} =$ 1.25V

10. Monitor the voltage drop across R_1 as R_2 is varied from its highest resistance value to its lowest resistance value.

    Lowest voltage value of R_1 _____

    Highest voltage value of R_1 _____

11. State your observations about the change in resistance versus the voltage change across R_1. State what was happening to the total circuit current value as the resistance of R_2 was made larger or smaller.

Discussion   As the resistance value of R_2 was decreased, the voltage across R_1 should have increased; conversely, as the resistance value of R_2 was increased the voltage across R_1 should have decreased. This indicates what is happening to the total circuit current. An increase in voltage indicates an increase in current and a decrease in voltage indicates a decrease in current.

---

12. **Turn off the power supply.**

    Remove R_2 and adjust it for 2.7 kΩ.

    Reconnect R_2.

13. Turn on the power supply.

14. Monitor the V_{R_3} as R_2 is varied from its highest resistance value to its lowest resistance value.

    Lowest voltage value across R_3 _____

    Highest voltage value across R_3 _____

15. State what you observed about V_{R_3} as R_2 was varied. Then state what was happening to the current value through R_3 as the resistance of R_2 was made larger or smaller.

Discussion   The observations should have been the same as noted in the previous Discussion.

---

16. Did the voltage drop across R_1 change more or less than the voltage drop across R_3?

    Did the current through R_1 change more or less than the current through R_3?

     Note   Determine what the change in voltage was across each resistor, then divide the change in voltage value by the resistance value.

17. Repeat Step 11. Monitor the voltage drop across R_4 as R_2 is varied from its highest resistance value to its lowest resistance value.

    Lowest voltage value across R_4 _____

    Highest voltage value across R_4 _____

18. State your observations about the change in voltage across R_4 versus the change in resistance of R_2. As the resistance value of R_2 was increased what happened to the current through R_4 or the total circuit current? What was happening to the current value through R_4 as R_2 was increased or decreased? Include in the observations whether the changes noted were larger or smaller than observed in the two previous procedures.

19. **Turn off the power supply.**

    Remove R_2, adjust it for 2.7 kΩ and reconnect the resistor into the circuit.

20. Connect the voltmeter across R_1. Turn on the power supply.

21. Monitor the voltage across R_1 as R_5 is varied from its lowest limit to its highest limit.

    Lowest voltage value across R_1 _____

    Highest voltage value across R_1 _____

22. State your observations about the changes in total circuit resistance and the total circuit current as R_5 was varied.

23. State what happened to the voltage across R_3 and R_4 as R_5 was varied. Be sure to correlate the increase or decrease of the resistance value R_5 to the changes in total circuit current, resistor currents, and voltages.

24. **Turn off the power supply.** Remove one lead of the power supply from the circuit.

    Place the ohmmeter across R_3 and vary the resistance of R_5 to its lowest limit and its highest limit.

    Lowest resistance value _____

    Highest resistance value _____

25. State what was observed concerning the change in resistance indication across R_3 as R_5 was varied. Include in the observations why the change in resistance occurred across R_3.

 Note Review how the total circuit resistance was determined.

Observations

1. Based on your observations in steps 10, 14, 17, 21, and 24, state what happened to total circuit current as the resistance, either R_2 or R_5, was made larger. Also indicate other currents or voltages that increased, decreased, or remained the same as a result of changing R_2 or R_5.

   Steps 10, 14, and 17:

   Steps 21 and 24:

2. Based on your observations in steps 10, 14, 17, 21, and 24, state what happened to total circuit current as the resistance either R_2 or R_5 was made smaller. Also indicate other currents or voltages that increased, decreased, or remained the same as a result of changing R_2 or R_5.

   Steps 10, 14, and 17:

   Steps 21 and 24:

3. In Step 24 the resistance across R_3 was monitored as R_5 was varied. Using this observation, state what would happen to total circuit current if R_3 was the resistance increasing in value.

What would happen to the voltage across R_3?

What would happen to the current through the series combination of R_4 and R_5.

Resistive Series Parallel Circuits: Level III

Name_____ Class_____ Date _____

Objectives	Upon completion of this experiment, you should be able to:

- Observe changes in total resistance as a resistor in the circuit opens or shorts.

- Determine changes in total circuit current and branch currents by monitoring changes in component voltages as a resistor in the circuit opens or shorts.

Text Reference Terrell, *Fundamentals of Electronics: DC/AC Circuits*
Chapter 6, Sections 6-1 through 6-4 and Section 6-6

Materials Required Variable power supply; 0 to 20 volts dc
Ohmmeter
Voltmeter
4.7-kΩ resistor
3.3-kΩ resistor
2.7-kΩ resistors (2)
2.2-kΩ resistor
1-kΩ resistors (2)
Various test leads

Introduction

Normally resistors do not short; however, other types of circuit components short or decrease their resistance when they become faulty.

By observing changes in voltage across other components in the circuit, changes in component current and total circuit current can be observed. The variation in voltage, whether increasing or decreasing, is a result of changes in the resistance of the resistors.

Procedures

1. Construct the circuit shown in Figure 21-1.

2. Determine by calculation the total circuit resistance.

_____ Ω

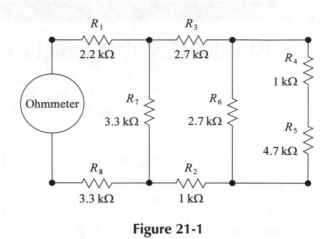

Figure 21-1

Discussion

A. Resistors R_4 and R_5 are in series.

B. The equivalent of R_4 and R_5 in series is in parallel with R_6.

C. Step B equivalent resistance is in series with R_3 and R_2.

D. Step C equivalent resistance is in parallel with R_7.

E. Step D equivalent resistance is in series with R_1 and R_8.

---

3. Record the total circuit resistance, ohmmeter indication.

   Total circuit resistance = _____ Ω

Discussion   The indication should be around 7.6 kΩ.

   Answer all questions as if a dc power supply were connected to the circuit; assume a voltage of 20 volts dc. **Do not connect the power supply to the circuit at this time.**

---

4. If R_4 shorted, what would happen to the total circuit resistance?

   Short R_4 by placing a jumper wire across the resistor. Record the ohmmeter indication.

   Ohmmeter indication = _____ Ω

   Did the ohmmeter indication show a decrease or increase in resistance?

   Would this indicate an increase or decrease in total circuit current?

   What would happen to the branch current through R_5?

Discussion A small decrease in total circuit resistance occurred; therefore, a small increase in total circuit current resulted. The current through R_5 increased due to a decrease in branch resistance.

5. Remove the jumper wire from R_4.

Remove R_4, leaving a gap where R_4 was connected.

What happened to the total circuit resistance?

Based on your observation of the ohmmeter indication, what would happen to the total circuit current?

What would happen to the branch current through R_5?

What would happen to the current through R_1?

What would happen to the branch current through R_6?

Discussion The total circuit current would decrease, because an increase in total resistance occurred. Therefore, the current through R_1 would decrease and the branch current through R_5 would be zero, because there is not a complete path for current. The equivalent resistance across R_7 would increase when R_4 opened. Therefore, the voltage across this equivalent resistance would increase even though the total circuit current decreased. The current through R_6 would increase.

However, the current changes would be small; note the small change in total circuit resistance. The branch with R_4 and R_5 has the largest resistance and any changes in this branch would have a small effect on the total circuit. If R_7, which has the smallest branch resistance, were to change, larger changes would occur in the circuit.

6. Reconnect R_4 in the circuit.

Place a jumper wire across R_7.

Did the total circuit resistance change a greater amount or smaller amount than when R_4 was shorted?

How would this effect total circuit current?

Would there be any branch current through R_6?

Would there be any voltage across R_3?

If the voltage across R_1 were added to the voltage across R_8, what would the value equal?

7. Remove the short from across R_7.

Remove R_7 and leave a gap where R_7 was installed.

What happened to the total circuit resistance value, using the original value as a reference (Step 3)?

What would happen to total circuit current?

Would the current through R_2 increase or decrease?

Did the voltage across R_2 increase or decrease?

Did the current through R_4 change?

Did the voltage across R_4 change?

8. Reconnect R_7 in the circuit.

9. Remove the ohmmeter and replace it with a 20-volt dc source, as shown in Figure 21-2.

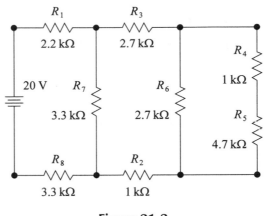

Figure 21-2

10. Measure and record the voltage drop across each resistor, using Table 21-1 to record the measured values.

RESISTOR	MEASURED VOLTAGE VALUE
R_1	
R_2	
R_3	
R_4	
R_5	
R_6	
R_7	
R_8	

Table 21-1

11. **Turn off the power supply.**

Place a jumper wire across R_4.

Turn the power supply on.

Measure the voltage across R_1. $V_{R_1} = $ _____ volts

Was the change in voltage across R_1 a large change or a small change?

Measure the voltage across R_5. V_{R_5} = _____ volts

Was the change in voltage across R_5 a large change or a small change?

12. **Turn off the power supply.**

Remove the jumper wire that is across R_4.

Remove R_4, leaving a gap where R_4 was connected.

Turn the power supply on.

What would happen to the voltage across R_5?

Measure the voltage across R_3. V_{R_3} = _____ volts

Was the change in voltage across R_3 a large change or a small change?

Discussion   The change in voltage across R_1 indicates that a change in total circuit current occurred. However, the change in voltage should have been small when R_4 was shorted. Even when R_4 was open, the changes were small, meaning the change in voltage was less than one volt.

Because the parallel branch that has R_4 has a large resistance, it had little effect on the total circuit current, but it did have an effect. **When the voltage changes are small but noticeable, start checking the high resistance parallel branches for faults first**

Notice that the parallel branch that has R_3 is the smallest parallel branch resistance.

---

13. **Turn off the power supply.**

Reinstall R_4 into the circuit.

14. Place a jumper wire across R_7.

Turn on the power supply and measure the voltage across R_5. State the reason for the indicated value.

V_{R_5} = _____ volts

Measure the voltage across R_1 and state the reason for the indicated value.

$V_{R_1} = $ _____ volts

15. **Turn off the power supply.**

Remove the jumper wire across R_7.

Remove R_7, leaving a gap where R_7 was connected.

Turn on the power supply.

16. Measure the voltage drops across R_2 and R_4. Does this indication agree with the answers to the questions about the voltage across R_2 and R_4 in Step 7?

$V_{R_2} = $ _____ volts

$V_{R_4} = $ _____ volts

Explain the voltmeter indication: i.e., the voltage increased/decreased because the total current ... etc.

Observations

1. State your observations about the changes in total circuit current, component voltages, and total circuit resistance, if the faults or changes in resistance occur in the parallel branch that has the largest resistance.

2. State your observations about the changes in total circuit current, component voltages, and total circuit resistance, if the faults or changes in resistance occur in the parallel branch that has the smallest resistance.

Series-Parallel Circuits: Level IV

Name_____ Class_____ Date_____

Objective Upon completion of this experiment, you should be able to:

- Troubleshooting series-parallel circuits.

Text Reference Terrell, *Fundamentals of Electronics: DC/AC Circuits*
  Chapter 6, Sections 6-1 through 6-4

Materials Required 330-Ω resistor
470-Ω resistor
820-Ω resistor
1-kΩ resistor
1.2-kΩ resistor
1.5-kΩ resistor
2.2-kΩ (2) resistors
2.7-kΩ resistor
3.3-kΩ resistor
3.9-kΩ resistor
4.7-kΩ resistor
5.6-kΩ resistor
10-kΩ resistor
12-kΩ resistor
Ohmmeter
Voltmeter
Current meter
Various test leads
Dual variable power supply; 0 volts to 20 volts per supply

Introduction

A series-parallel circuit is the most common type of electronic configuration. This type of circuit includes the characteristics of both a series circuit and a parallel circuit. Therefore, with a good understanding of series and parallel circuits, the combination of these two (the series-parallel circuit) should be fairly simple to master. Important points to remember about the characteristics of series and parallel circuits are:

- In a series circuit, current is the same in all series components.

- In a parallel circuit, the voltages across parallel components are equal.

- The beginning point in analyzing a series-parallel circuit is to first determine which components are in series and which components are in parallel.

Refer to Figure 22-1. A close look at the schematic diagram should reveal the following points:

- R_1 and R_2 are in parallel.

- R_3, R_7, and R_{11} are in series.

- R_8, R_9, and R_{10} are in parallel.

- R_5 and R_6 are in series.

The equivalent resistance of R_5 and R_6 (the sum of R_5 and R_6) is in parallel with R_4.

After determining the above facts, and knowing the characteristics of a series circuit and a parallel circuit, the following statements are true:

- The voltage drops across R_1 and R_2 are equal.

- The current through R_3, R_7, and R_{11} is the same.

- The voltage drops across R_8, R_9, and R_{10} are equal.

- The current through R_5 is equal to the current through R_6.

- The voltage drop across R_4 is equal to the sum of the voltage drops across R_5 and R_6.

The first step in estimating all the resistor voltage drops is to determine the total resistance of the circuit. This can be accomplished if the circuit is reduced to a simple series circuit.

To find the equivalent resistance of any resistors in parallel, use the product over the sum formula, or use the reciprocal formula. Once the equivalent parallel resistance has been determined, add the equivalent resistance to any resistor in series. Repeat the process until the total resistance is known.

After the equivalent total resistance is found, Ohm's Law can be used to determine the total circuit current. The total current is then multiplied by each resistor in the equivalent series circuit to determine the individual voltage drops and individual current through each resistor.

Procedures

1. Refer to the schematic shown in Figure 22-1 at the beginning of the "Observations" section of this experiment. Reduce the circuit to an equivalent series circuit and then calculate the individual voltage drop across each resistor and the amount of current that flows through each resistor. Fill out the calculation columns in Table 22-1.

COMPONENT	CALCULATED VALUES		MEASURED VALUES	
	VOLTAGE	CURRENT	VOLTAGE	CURRENT
R_1				
R_2				
R_3				
R_4				
R_5				
R_6				
R_7				
R_8				
R_9				
R_{10}				
R_{11}				

Table 22-1

Compare your estimated values with other lab teams and discuss differences.

Discussion   If working as a lab team, one member should construct Figure 22-1 while the other member constructs Figure 22-2. Each of the figures must be constructed to answer the Observation questions.

If working alone, construct Figure 22-1, fill in the table information and then answer the Observation questions that pertain to this figure. Then construct Figure 22-2, fill in the information required for Table 22-2 and answer the Observation questions concerning this figure. The Observation questions are grouped together by figure number to simplify the process.

---

2. Construct the circuit shown in Figure 22-1. Connect the black terminal of one power supply to the red terminal of the **second (2nd)** power supply. Then connect the red terminal of the first power supply and the black terminal of the second power supply to the circuit. Measure between the two leads for 40 volts.

3. Measure the individual voltage drops and the current through each resistor.

   Complete the measurement columns of Table 22-1. If the calculated values do not agree with the measured values, re-evaluate and re-measure until the differences are resolved.

   If you are working alone, answer the "Observations" that refer to Figure 22-2 before proceeding.

4. Refer to the schematic diagram shown in Figure 22-2. Calculate the current that flows through each resistor and the individual voltage drop across each resistor. Complete the calculated columns in Table 22-2.

COMPONENT	CALCULATED VALUES		MEASURED VALUES	
	VOLTAGE	CURRENT	VOLTAGE	CURRENT
R_1				
R_2				
R_3				
R_4				
R_5				
R_6				
R_7				
R_8				
R_9				
R_{10}				
R_{11}				

Table 22-2

Compare your estimated values with other lab teams and discuss differences.

5. Construct the circuit in Figure 22-2. Measure the individual voltage drops and the current that flows through each resistor. Complete the measurement columns of Table 22-2. If the measured values do not agree with the estimated values, determine which is correct.

Observations

Answer the following questions to test your understanding of the two series-parallel circuits and previous lab experiments. After answering the question, prove the answer by measuring the currents or voltages required to answer the question. If the question pertains to the total circuit resistance, remember to disconnect the power supply before using the ohmmeter.

1. Refer to Figure 22-1. The total circuit current will flow through which of the following resistors: (Circle all that apply.)

   a. R_1, R_3, and R_7

   b. R_3, R_7, R_9, and R_{11}

   c. R_3, R_7, and R_{11}

   d. None of the above

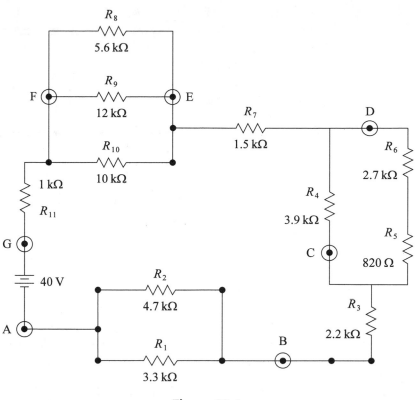

Figure 22-1

2. Refer to Figure 22-1. The sum of the currents through R_1 and R_2 is equal to: (Circle all that apply.)

    a. the current that flows through Point B

    b. the total circuit current

    c. the current that flows through R_5

3. Refer to Figure 22-1. The same value of current flows through resistors R_{11} and R_5. _____

    a. True

    b. False

4. Refer to Figure 22-1. The voltage drop across R_4 is equal to the sum of the voltage drops across R_5 and R_6. _____

    a. True

    b. False

5. Refer to Figure 22-1. What voltage drops could be added together to equal the supply voltage? (*Hint:* draw all current paths)

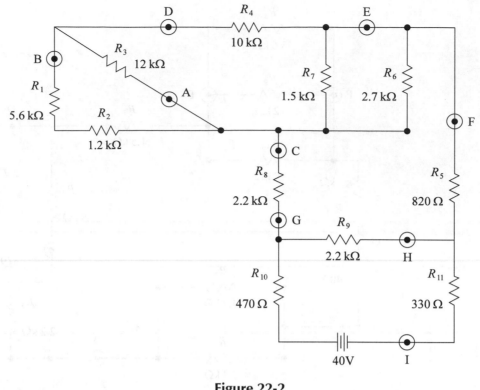

Figure 22-2

Example $V_{R_{11}} + V_{R_8} + V_{R_7} + V_{R_4} + V_{R_3} + V_{R_2} = 12$ volts

List the other sets of voltage drops, that their sum is equal to the applied voltage.

6. Refer to Figure 22-1. The current entering Point C is equal to _____.

   a. the same value as the current through R_3 and R_7

   b. the sum of the currents through R_5 and R_4

   c. the difference between the currents through R_3 and R_5.

7. Refer to Figure 22-1. If R_{11} were to open, the total circuit current would _____.

    a. increase to a very large value

    b. remain the same

    c. decrease to zero

8. Refer to Figure 22-1. If R_8 were to open, the total circuit resistance would _____.

    a. increase

    b. decrease

    c. remain the same

9. Refer to Figure 22-1. If R_1 were to open, the total circuit current would _____.

    a. increase

    b. decrease

    c. remain the same

10. Refer to Figure 22-1. If resistor R_7 were to increase to 15 kΩ, the voltage across R_7 would _____.

    a. increase

    b. decrease

    c. remain the same

11. Refer to Figure 22-2. Resistors R_{10} and R_{11} have the same value of current flowing through them. _____

    a. True

    b. False

12. Refer to Figure 22-2. The current at Point D is equal to the current at Point F. _____

    a. True

    b. False

13. Refer to Figure 22-2. Circle all of the following statements that are true.

    a. The current at Point C equals the current at Point F.

    b. The current at Point E plus the current through R_6 equals the current at Point F.

    c. The current at Point B plus the current at Point E plus the current at Point A equals the current at Point C.

d. The current at Point I minus the current at Point H equals the current at Point F.

e. The voltage across R_9 is equal to the applied voltage minus the sum of the voltages across R_{11} and R_{10}.

14. Refer to Figure 22-2. Resistor R_5 is in series with R_8. _____

   a. True

   b. False

15. Refer to Figure 22-2. Which resistor will have the total circuit current flowing through it? _____

   a. R_5

   b. R_{10}

   c. R_4

   d. R_8

16. Refer to Figure 22-2. A voltmeter measurement at Point A in reference to Point E would have an indication of:

   _____ volts

17. Refer to Figure 22-2. A voltmeter measurement at Point C in reference to Point E would have an indication of:

   _____ volts

18. Refer to Figure 22-2. A voltmeter measurement at Point F in reference to Point I would have an indication of:

   _____ volts

19. Refer to Figure 22-2. A voltmeter measurement at Point G in reference to Point A would have an indication of:

   _____ volts

20. Refer to Figure 22-2. A voltmeter measurement at Point B in reference to Point E would have an indication of:

   _____ volts

21. Refer to Figure 22-2. A voltmeter measurement at Point I in reference to Point E would have an indication of:

   _____ volts

22. Refer to Figure 22-2. A voltmeter measurement at Point H in reference to Point I would have an indication of:

   _____ volts

23. Refer to Figure 22-2. If R_4 were to open, the voltage across R_3 would _____.

    a. decrease to zero volts

    b. increase to the applied voltage

    c. remain the same value

24. Refer to Figure 22-2. If R_7 were to open, the total circuit current would _____.

    a. increase

    b. decrease

    c. remain the same value

25. Refer to Figure 22-2. If R_5 were to open, the total circuit current would _____.

    a. decrease to zero

    b. decrease to 13.33 mA

    c. increase

    d. remain the same value

Series-Parallel Circuits: Voltage Dividers; Level IV

Name_____ Class_____ Date _____

Objectives	Upon completion of this experiment, you should be able to:

- Observe the characteristics of a voltage divider circuit—unloaded.
- Observe the characteristics of a loaded voltage divider—the effect on total circuit current, individual voltage drops, and total circuit resistance.

Text Reference	Terrell, *Fundamentals of Electronics: DC/AC Circuits*

        Chapter 4, Section 4-7
        Chapter 6, Section 6-5

Materials Required	Voltmeter

Variable power supply; 0 to 20 volts dc
1-kΩ resistor
2-kΩ resistor
3.3-kΩ resistor
4.7-kΩ resistor
10-kΩ resistor
Various test leads

Introduction

In a series circuit the resistors divide the voltage, dependent on the relative size of the resistor. All of the resistors have the same value of current and the sum of the voltage drops is equal to the applied voltage.

When a resistor is placed in parallel with one of the series resistances, all of the characteristics of the circuit change. An alternate current path is created, meaning that not all the resistors have the same current value flowing through them. A series-parallel circuit has been connected and all of the characteristics learned in the previous series-parallel circuits experiments apply.

In this experiment we will explore this concept and you will learn how a resistor can be used as a "load" on the existing circuit, thereby changing its characteristics. The loaded voltage divider is a useful circuit for the right application.

The "Observations" are included in the "Procedures". In this format the circuit is connected and answers can be checked as the procedures are performed.

Procedures

1. Connect the circuit shown in Figure 23-1.

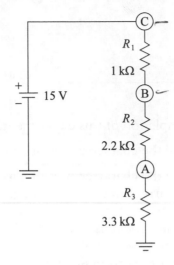

Figure 23-1

2. Measure the voltage at each indicated point in the circuit and record the voltage drops in Table 23-1.

VOLTAGE POINT	VOLTAGE VALUE
Point A	2.28 V
Point B	5.08 V
Point C	7.65 V

Table 23-1

3. Determine the voltage across each resistor from the information in Table 23-1 and record the information in Table 23-2.

RESISTOR	VOLTAGE VALUE
R_1	13.02 V
R_2	12.73 V
R_3	7.65 V

Table 23-2

4. Determine the total circuit resistance and the total circuit current from the values listed in Table 23-1 and Table 23-2.

Total circuit current 2.33 mA

Total circuit resistance 6.42K Ω

5. While monitoring the voltage at Point A, insert R_{L1} as shown in Figure 23-2.

   State your observations and conclusions as to what values in the circuit changed to cause a change in the voltage at Point A. Show the current paths that will flow through each resistor in Figure 23-2.

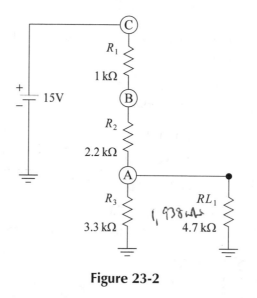

Figure 23-2

6. With R_{L1} still in the circuit, measure the voltage at each point in the circuit and record the voltage drops in Table 23-3.

VOLTAGE POINT	VOLTAGE VALUE
Point A	5.02V
Point B	~~15.8V~~ 12.12V
Point C	~~10.84V~~ 5.68V

Table 23-3

7. Determine the voltage across each resistor from the information in Table 23-3 and record the information in Table 23-4.

RESISTOR	VOLTAGE VALUE
R_1	2.89V
R_2	6.44 V
R_3	5.68V
R_{L1}	5.68V

Table 23-4

8. Determine the total circuit resistance and the total circuit current from the values listed in Table 23-3 and Table 23-4.

   Total circuit current   2.9   mA

   Total circuit resistance   5.13 K   Ω

9. Compare the values in Steps 4 and 8 and state why the values in Step 8 changed when resistor R_{L1} was added.

   Voltage is proportional to resistance. Total resistance dropped due to the parallel connection created by R_{L1} w/ R_3 when the total resistance decreased voltage across the series resistors went down due to the "loaded" resistor. Current is inversly proportional to resistance. So the current increased across the circuit

10. Determine the current values through each resistor, using the values from Table 23-4.

   I_{R_1} = 2.89 mA
   I_{R_2} = 2.92 mA
   I_{R_3} = 1.7 mA
   $I_{R_{L1}}$ = 1.2 mA

11. What two currents summed together equal the total circuit current?

   The currents of R_3 & R_{L1}

12. What resistor(s) have the total circuit current flowing through them?

   R_1 & R_2

13. Why did the voltage across R_1 and R_2 change?

Because resistance decreased due to loaded R_{L_1}, the voltage across the (2) resistors dropped proportionally

14. While monitoring the voltage at Point B, insert R_{L2} into the circuit as shown in Figure 23-3.

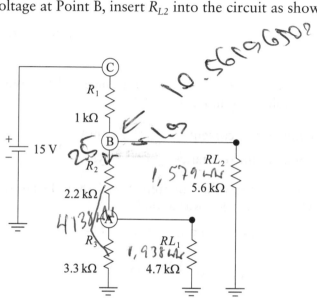

Figure 23-3

15. State your observations and conclusions as to why the voltage at Point B changed. Show the current paths through each resistor in the circuit shown in Figure 23-3.

16. Measure the voltage at each point in the circuit and record the voltage drops in Table 23-5.

VOLTAGE POINT	VOLTAGE VALUE
Point A	4.92 V
Point B	9.24 V
Point C	15.02 V

Table 23-5

17. Determine the voltage drop across each resistor from the information in Table 23-5 and record the information in Table 23-6.

RESISTOR	VOLTAGE VALUE
R_1	4.40 V
R_2	5.64 V
R_3	4.97 V
R_{L1}	4.97
R_{L2}	10.61

Table 23-6

18. Determine the total circuit resistance and the total circuit current from the values listed in Table 23-5 and Table 23-6.

Total circuit current ~~8~~ 4.4 mA

Total circuit resistance ~~1.5 K~~ Ω 3,379 3.4 KΩ

19. Compare the values in Steps 8 and 18 and state why the values in Step 18 changed when resistor R_{L2} was added.

Since resistance decreased again voltage went down. The current then increased

Observations

1. Determine the current values through each resistor, using the values from Table 23-6.

I_{R_1} = 4.4 mA
I_{R_2} = 2.5 mA
I_{R_3} = 1.5 mA
$I_{R_{L1}}$ = 1.05 mA
$I_{R_{L2}}$ = 1.9 mA

2. What three currents summed together equal the total circuit current?

R_3 R_{L1} & R_{L2}

3. How many resistors does the total circuit current flow through?

R_1

Discussion The voltage at each point changed as the load requirements changed. When a new load resistor was added, the total circuit resistance changed; the current through the individual voltage divider resistors changed, changing the voltage across them. If more load resistors were added, a further change in the original voltages across the resistors would also occur.

If a constant voltage is required for a load resistance that varies, the loaded voltage divider is unable to provide a constant voltage. With a fixed load resistance, the loaded voltage divider can provide a constant voltage.

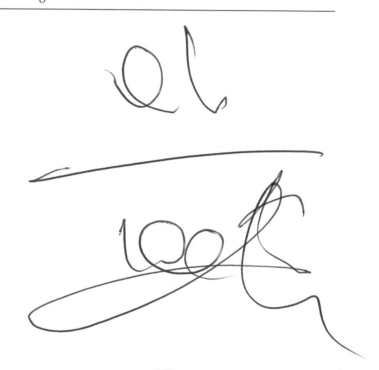

Series-Parallel Circuits: Resistive Bridge Circuits; Level VI

Name_____ Class_____ Date _____

Objectives   Upon completion of this experiment, you should be able to:

- Observe the characteristics of a balanced resistive bridge, commonly referred to as a Wheatstone Bridge.

- Determine, by experimentation, whether an unknown resistance is larger or smaller than the resistor required to balance a resistive bridge.

Text Reference   Terrell, *Fundamentals of Electronics; DC/AC Circuits*
    Chapter 6, Section 6-5

Materials Required   Voltmeter
    Ohmmeter
    Current meter*
    Variable power supply; 0 to 20 volts dc
    Three (3) 1-kΩ resistors
    5-kΩ variable resistor
    Various test leads

_____

* The current meter required for this experiment is a zero-centered analog meter or a non-polarity sensitive DMM. The meter must be able to read at least 20 mA.

Introduction

The Wheatstone bridge or resistive bridge is another application of a series-parallel circuit. If the bridge is balanced, the voltage difference between two points is zero volts. Refer to Figure 24-1 located under "Procedures," Step 1.

If the ratio of the resistors is the same:

$$\frac{R_1}{R_2} = \frac{R_3}{R_X}$$

The difference of potential between Points A and B is zero volts. If a current meter is placed between Points A and B, no current indication will be observed. This condition is called balancing the bridge.

If the bridge is not balanced, a potential difference will exist and the current meter will indicate some value. The direction of current and the value of current can be used to determine the value of R_X if it is not known. This experiment explores this concept and how to use it to find an unknown value of resistance.

Procedures

1. Construct the circuit shown in Figure 24-1.

   CAUTION Adjust the power supply for 10 volts before connecting it to the circuit and then turn it off.

   Try to match the resistance of the three 1-kΩ resistors as closely as possible.

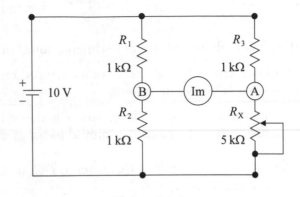

Figure 24-1

2. Place the current meter between Points A and B, placing the common or black lead at Point A.

   Turn on the power supply.

   Adjust the rheostat until the current indication is zero milliamps.

3. Measure the voltage across each resistor in the circuit and record the values in Table 24-1.

RESISTOR NOMENCLATURE	VOLTAGE VALUE
R_1	
R_2	
R_3	
R_X	

Table 24-1

4. State your observations concerning the voltage drops across the resistors and the difference of potential between Points A and B.

Discussion The difference of potential between Points A and B should be zero. Even though the voltage on each side of the current meter is five volts, the difference is zero. The zero current indication indicates a balanced bridge meaning that:

$$\frac{R_1}{R_2} = \frac{R_3}{R_X}$$

This occurs only when the bridge is balanced.

5. **Turn off the power supply.** Remove the rheostat and adjust it for 500 Ω. Reinsert the rheostat and turn on the power supply.

6. The current meter should indicate about 2 mA, with no negative sign. Measure each resistor voltage drop and record the value in Table 24-2.

RESISTOR	VOLTAGE VALUE
R_1	
R_2	
R_3	
R_X	

Table 24-2

Discussion *Using a Non-Polarity Sensitive DMM* The "polarity" of the current has no meaning except to indicate direction of current flow. If there is no sign, it indicates that the electron current flow is going into the black lead and out the red lead of the DMM. If a negative is indicated on the DMM, the current is flowing into the red lead and out of the black lead.

Using a Zero-Centered Analog Meter The needle should have deflected to the right, indicating electron current flow is going into the black lead and out the red lead.

Because the current is flowing from Point A to Point B, R_X is smaller than R_2. The smallest resistor in a parallel circuit will have the largest current. The current values through R_1 and R_3 will be equal; having equal resistors and equal voltage drops.

Because the current meter has a finite value of resistance, the difference of potential between Points A and B drops across the meter. This causes a current to flow from the less positive side to the more positive side. In this case, R_X is smaller than R_2, therefore V_{R_X} is less than V_{R_2}.

The value of the unknown resistor R_X can be determined by the following equations:

$$\frac{V_{RX} R_2}{(2V_{R1} - V_{R2})} = R_X$$

Using the above equation, the value for R_X is 500 Ω. This can be useful for finding unknown values of component resistances. One word of caution: Resistors R_1, R_2, and R_3 must be the same stated value and the accuracy of the reading will be determined by how closely R_1, R_2, and R_3 match each other. The finite resistance of the current meter will also determine the accuracy of the reading. The higher the resistance of the meter the less accurate the indication.

Because this is a linear function, a scale could be established to determined unknown resistance values. When 2 mA of current flow from Point A to Point B, R_X will always be 500 Ω.

7. **Turn off the power supply.** Remove the rheostat and adjust it for 2 kΩ.

8. Turn on the power supply and record the indicated current.

    Current meter _____ mA

    Record each resistor voltage in Table 24-3.

RESISTOR	VOLTAGE VALUE
R_1	
R_2	
R_3	
R_X	

Table 24-3

9. Determine the value of R_X, using the equation stated above.

    $R_X =$ _____ Ω

Discussion   This time the current indication was about -1.4 mA, indicating that V_{R_2} was less than V_{R_X}.

   The determined value of R_X should have been close to 2 kΩ.

10. Adjust the rheostat for some smaller value and repeat Steps 8 and 9.

    Current meter _____ mA

    Record each resistor voltage in Table 24-4.

RESISTOR	VOLTAGE VALUE
R_1	
R_2	
R_3	
R_X	

Table 24-4

Determine the value of R_X, using the equation stated above.

$R_X =$ _____ Ω

11. **Now turn off the power supply** and remove the rheostat.

Measure the value of R_X with an ohmmeter to determine the accuracy of the determination.

Observation

1. Show, by calculation, why the current flows from Point A to Point B when R_X is smaller that the other resistors in the circuit. (Hint: Determine and compare I_{R_3}, I_{R_X}, and I_{R_1}.)

Multiple Voltage Sources: Level I

Name_____ Class_____ Date_____

Objectives   Upon completion of this experiment, you should be able to:

• Analyze circuits with multiple voltages sources by determining the total
circuit voltage, the total circuit current, and the component voltages drops.

Text   Terrell, *Fundamentals of Electronics: DC/AC Circuits*
Reference   Chapter 4, Section 4-6

Materials   Dual variable power supply; 0 to 20 volts dc
Required   Current meter
Voltmeter
330-Ω resistor
680-Ω resistor
880-Ω resistor
1-kΩ resistor
2.7-kΩ resistor
Various test leads

Introduction

The technique used in this and the following experiment is just one of several
that could be used to solve for circuit unknowns in multiple voltage source
circuits, both series-aiding and series-opposing.

In this experiment the first objective will be to find the total circuit voltage. You
will then solve for the total circuit resistance, and finally, you will solve for the
total circuit current.

Once the total circuit current is found, the individual voltage drops can be
determined.

Procedures

1. Construct the circuit shown in Figure 25-1.

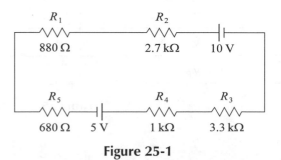

Figure 25-1

2. Determine the theoretical values listed in Table 25-1.

Discussion   The total circuit voltage can be found by determining the direction of current for each source. If the two currents go in the same direction, find the sum of the voltage sources. If the currents go in opposite directions, find the difference between the two sources and take the polarity of the larger one.

Redraw the circuit using the sum or difference voltage as one voltage source and solve the circuit unknowns the same way you would solve any series circuit.

VALUES TO BE DETERMINED	THEORETICAL VALUES
Total Resistance	
Total Circuit Voltage	
Total Circuit Current	
V_{R_1}	
V_{R_2}	
V_{R_3}	
V_{R_4}	
V_{R_5}	

Table 25-1

3. Using the current meter and voltmeter, measure the values listed in Table 25-2.

Discussion   Determine the total circuit voltage by the sum of the voltage drops across the resistors. The direction of current can be found by measuring the voltage polarity across one resistor. The polarity of voltage is determined by the direction of current. If the voltages are opposing, use the polarity of the larger source. If the polarity of the voltage sources are the same, the direction of current will be the same for both sources.

VALUES TO BE MEASURED	MEASURED VALUES
I_T	
V_{R_1}	
V_{R_2}	
V_{R_3}	
V_{R_4}	
V_{R_5}	
V_{Total}	

Table 25-2

4. Compare the results listed in Table 25-1 and 25-2 and state your observations about the differences in values, current direction, sum of the voltage drops, and individual voltage drops.

Observations

Using Figure 25-2 as a reference, answer the following questions. If you are in doubt or encounter trouble answering the following questions, connect the circuit and make the appropriate measurements to confirm the answers.

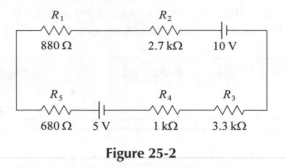

Figure 25-2

1. Are the voltage sources in Figure 25-2 opposing or aiding?

2. What is the total circuit voltage in Figure 25-2?

3. Is the direction of current in Figure 25-2 CW or CCW?

4. Is the voltage across R_2 in Figure 25-2 larger or smaller than the voltage across R_2 in Figure 25-1?

5. Is the polarity of the voltage across R_2 in Figure 25-2 the same as the polarity of the voltage across R_2 in Figure 25-1?

6. If the 5-volt source in Figure 25-2 was increased to 10 volts, what would the sum of the voltage drops equal?

7. In Figure 25-2, if R_4 were to open, what voltage would be measured across the open?

8. If the 10-volt power source in Figure 25-2 was decreased to 5 volts, what would a current meter indicate?

9. If resistor R_3 in Figure 25-2 were to increase in value (about 10 times larger), would the total circuit voltage change?

   Explain your answer.

10. If resistor R_3 in Figure 25-2 were to increase in value (about 10 times larger), would the voltage across R_2 change?

    Explain your answer.

Multiple Voltage Sources: Level II

Name _____ Class _____ Date _____

Objectives   Upon completion of this experiment, you should be able to:

- Analyze complex multiple source circuits.

- Practice writing simple procedures for measuring desired values.

Text Reference   Terrell, *Fundamentals of Electronics: DC/AC Circuits*
Chapter 4, Section 4-6
Chapter 7, Section 7-5

Materials Required   Dual variable power supply; 0 to 20 volts dc
470-Ω resistor
880-Ω resistor
1-kΩ resistor
2.7-kΩ resistor
Current meter
Voltmeter
Various test leads

Introduction

Nodal analysis or Thévenin's Theorem may be used to determine the theoretical values of multiple-source circuits. The main focus of this experiment will be to determine the direction of current flow through each resistor and the voltage drop across each resistor by use of experimentation.

Some of the procedures for this project will be given and others will be written by the student. The procedures should include clearly stated steps to accomplish a given task. The procedural steps should be written so that a logical progression leads to a conclusion or observation. The steps should be written at a level that other students, with similar backgrounds, can follow and understand.

Procedures

1. Construct the circuit shown in Figure 26-1.

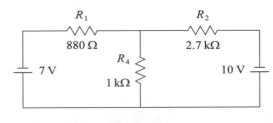

Figure 26-1

2. Determine the theoretical values for the values listed in Table 26-1.

VALUES TO BE DETERMINED	THEORETICAL VALUES
V_{R_1}	
V_{R_2}	
V_{R_4}	

Table 26-1

Discussion   Open resistor R_4 and solve the circuit using the procedures used in Experiment 25. Once the value of voltage across R_1 has been established, theoretically measure the voltage, with an infinite impedance voltmeter, at the gap left by an open R_4. Using the value of voltage across R_2 confirm that the measurement across an open R_4 is the same value.

$$+V_{R_1} + -7V = Voltage_{Thevenin} \text{ or } +V_{R_2} + -10V = V_{Thevenin}$$

Remove the power sources with R_4 still open, and replace the sources with a jumper wire. Then, with an ohmmeter, measure the total resistance at the gap left by an open R_4. This value is the Thévenin resistance. Using the Thévenin voltage and resistance, one source and one resistance, connect R_4 to the circuit and solve for the voltage across R_4. This will be the voltage across R_4 in Figure 26-2.

When this voltage has been established, the remaining voltages can be determined. Remember that the voltage across R_4 is in parallel with the voltage across R_1 and the 7-volt source and also in parallel with R_2 and the 10-volt source.

3. Write a step-by-step set of procedures that can be used to measure the current through R_4 in Figure 26-1.

4. Use the procedures just completed to measure the value of current through R_4.

It may be necessary to add to or rewrite procedural steps to accomplish the task of measuring I_{R_4}.

$I_{R_4} =$ _____

Is the current flowing up or down through the resistor?

Would your procedures work for a DMM as well as a VOM?

 Note   Remember a VOM is a unidirectional device and most DMMs are bi-directional devices.

5. Write procedural steps to measure the voltage across each of the resistors.

 Note   In your procedural steps, indicate the proper polarity of the meter to match the polarity of the resistors. In other words, the red lead of the meter should be on the positive end of the resistor and the black or common lead of the meter should be on the negative end of the resistor. State how to properly connect these leads.

6. Use the procedures to fill in the blanks in Table 26-2, with actual measured values.

VALUES TO BE MEASURED	THEORETICAL VALUES
V_{R_1}	
V_{R_2}	
V_{R_4}	

Table 26-2

7. Prove Kirchhoff's Voltage Law by determining the algebraic sum of the voltages for the two current loops:

$$V_{R_1} + V_{R_4} - 7 \text{ volts} = 0 \text{ volts}$$
$$V_{R_2} + V_{R_4} - 10 \text{ volts} = 0 \text{ volts}$$

8. Prove Kirchhoff's Current Law by determining the algebraic sum of the currents through R_4.

$$\frac{V_{R1}}{R_1} + \frac{V_{R2}}{R_2} = I_{R4}$$

Observations

Using Figure 26-2 as a reference and the procedures stated and written by you, answer the following questions. It may be necessary to connect the circuit shown in Figure 26-2 and make measurements to confirm your answers.

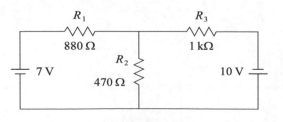

Figure 26-2

1. In Figure 26-1, the current through R_4 was larger than the current through either of the other resistors. Is this the case in Figure 26-2?

   Explain your answer.

2. Which resistor has the largest voltage drop in Figure 26-2?

3. The current is largest through which resistor in Figure 26-2?

4. If R_1 opens, what happens to the value of current through R_2 in Figure 26-2?

5. If R_2 opens, what is the total circuit voltage in Figure 26-2?

6. If the 7-volt source decreases in value, what happens to the value of current through R_2 in Figure 26-2?

   Explain your answer.

7. Can the equation stated in Step 8 be used to determine the current through R_2 in Figure 26-2? If the answer is no, state what **important** change(s) are necessary to use this equation?

8. Can the voltage equations stated in Step 7 be used to prove Kirchhoff's Voltage Law in Figure 26-2? If the answer is no, state what **important** change(s) are necessary to use this equation?

9. If the 7-volt dc source is increased to 10 volts, what will happen to the current through R_2 in Figure 26-2?

10. If the 7-volt dc source is increased to 10 volts, what will happen to the voltage across R_2 in Figure 26-2?

EQUIPMENT LIST

Digital Multimeter @ 10 MΩ input impedance

Volt-Ohm-Meter @ 20 kΩ/volt

Dual DC Power Supply @ 0 to 20 volts DC

Function Generator @ 50 Ω output impedance
DC offset on/off
Sine Wave . . Triangle Wave . . Square Wave
Percent Duty Cycle Adjustment
TTL Output

Dual-Trace Oscilloscope @ 20 MHz

OPTIONAL

1-10-100 mA Current Meter

Capacitance Meter

COMPONENTS

¼ W Resistor Kit	Capacitors	Variable Resistors
or	1000 µF 50 V	100 kΩ
	100 µF 50 V	20 kΩ
2 MΩ	10 µF 35 V (2)	10 kΩ (2)
100 kΩ	2.2 µF 35 V	5 kΩ
47 kΩ	0.22 µF 35 V	1 kΩ
10 kΩ	0.1 µF 35 V	
8.2 kΩ	0.033 µF 35 V	**Switches/Misc.**
6.8 kΩ	0.022 µF 35 V	
5.6 kΩ	0.01 µF 35 V	SPST switch
4.7 kΩ	0.0047 µF 35 V	SPDT switch
3.3 kΩ	0.0033 µF 35 V	Neon Tube NE2
2.7 kΩ (2)	0.0022 µF 35 V (2)	Red LED
2.2 kΩ	0.001 µF 35 V	Green LED
1.5 kΩ		
1 kΩ (3)	**Inductors**	12 volt DPDT relay
820 Ω		3 volt DPDT relay
680 Ω	4 to 7H	1N914 or 1N4148 (small
560 Ω	100 mH	signal diode)
470 Ω	33 mH	8 Ω speaker
330 Ω	10 mH	
220 Ω	1 mH	
180 Ω (2)		
150 Ω		
100 Ω		
56 Ω (2)		

Audio Transformer (Step down)
AC Power Supply or 12.6 VAC Power Transformer

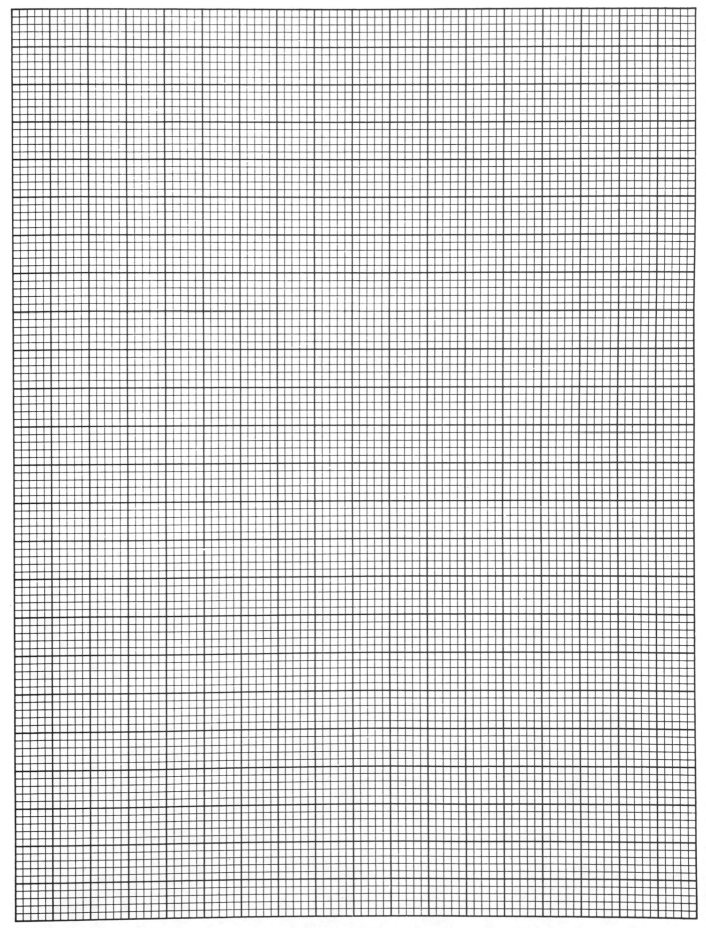

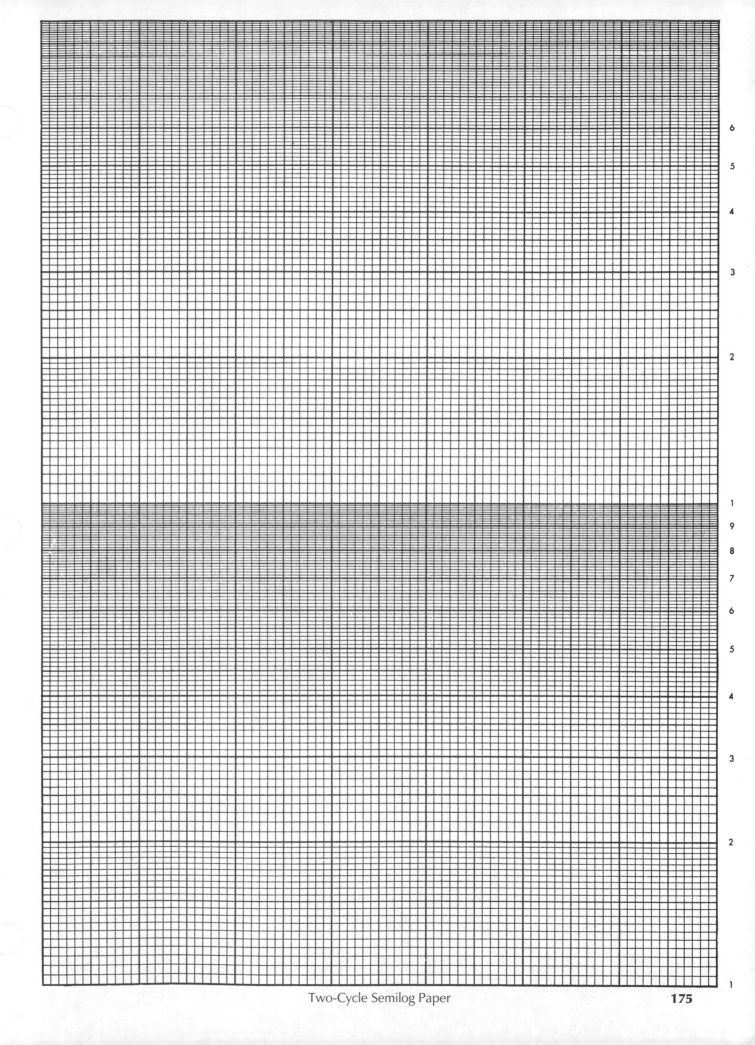

Two-Cycle Semilog Paper

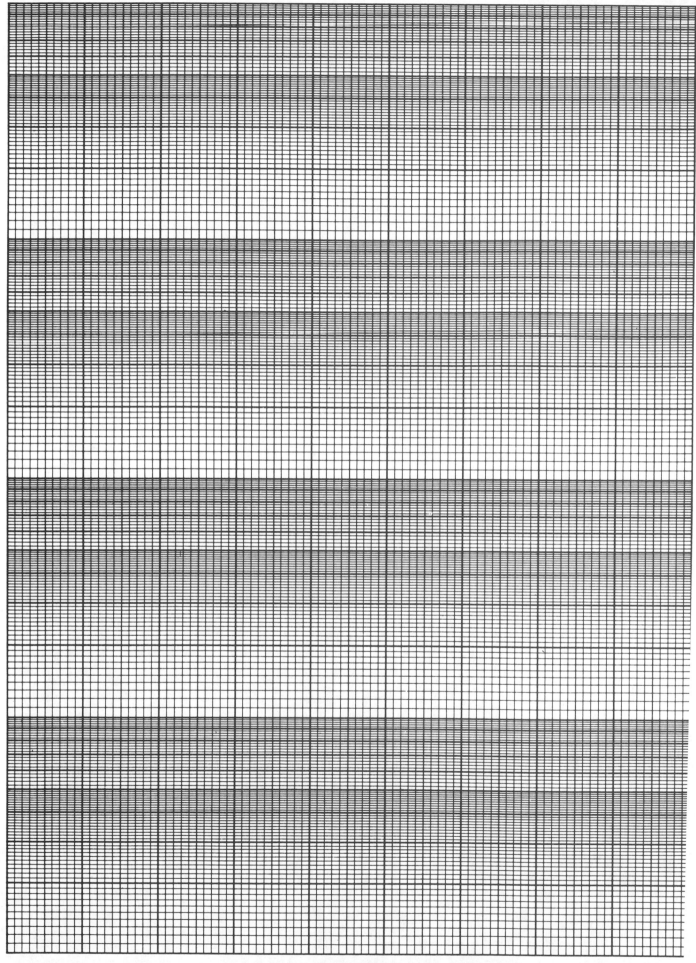

Four-Cycle Semilog Paper